W9-CHS-745

UNIT 6 Narrative 141

Voice Creating a Connection to the Audience 142

Word Choice Using Specific and
Accurate Words 150

Sentence Fluency Capturing Smooth
and Rhythmic Flow 158

UNIT 7 Persuasive 167

Ideas Using Details 168

Organization Ending With a Sense of Resolution 176

Voice Taking Risks to Create Voice 184

UNIT 8 Expository 193

Word Choice Choosing Words That
Deepen Meaning 194

Sentence Fluency Breaking the "Rules"
to Create Fluency 202

All Traits Putting the Traits Together 210

UNIT 9 Wrapping Up the Year 219

Reflecting on Myself as a Writer 220

Saying Good-bye to My Writing Folder 224

Celebrating Our Accomplishments 228

Cleaning Up and Having Fun 232

Student-Friendly Scoring Guides 234

SCHOLASTIC
Traits Writing™

Student Handbook

Credits

Cover: bl: © Ipatov/Shutterstock; p. 39 l: © Gary John Norman/Getty Images, r: © Fuse/Getty Images, b: © Hill Street Studios/Blend Images; p. 47: © Alaska Stock/Alamy; p. 55 l: © AVAVA/Shutterstock, r: © James Steidl/Shutterstock: © Masterfile; p. 65: © BESTWEB/Shutterstock, p. 73: © Findlay Rankin/ Photolibrary; p. 81: © Tom Grill /Getty Images; p. 91: © Branch Out/MediaBakery; p. 99 bl: © Gilmanshin /Shutterstock, tl: © Gilmanshin/Shutterstock, tr: © Pavel Ignatov/Shutterstock, br: © Kitch Bain/ Shutterstock; p. 107: © Stuart Pitkin/iStockphoto; p. 117: © Jazzyqt/iStockphoto; p. 125: © Cathy Keifer/ Shutterstock; p. 133: © Allen Einstein/NBAE via Getty Images; p. 143: © Arch White/Alamy; p. 151: © Stewart Cohen Pictures/Getty Images; p. 159: © Christophe Elise/Icon SMI/Corbis; p. 169: © Dorling Kindersley/ Getty Images; p. 177: © Dave and Les Jacobs/Blend Images; p. 185: © Ipatov/Shutterstock; p. 195: © Yakobchuk Vasyl/Shutterstock; p. 203: © Masterfile; p. 211: © Shannon Fagan/Getty Images

Trait Mates Illustrations: Wook Jin Jung

Contents

UNIT 1 Getting Started 5

The Writing Process 6

Prewriting 12

Drafting 18

Revising 24

Editing 30

UNIT 2 Expository 37

Ideas Finding a Topic 38

Organization Creating the Lead 46

Voice Establishing a Tone 54

UNIT 3 Narrative 63

Word Choice Applying Strong Verbs 64

Sentence Fluency Crafting Well-Built Sentences 72

Ideas Focusing the Topic 80

UNIT 4 Persuasive 89

Organization Using Sequence Words
and Transition Words 90

Voice Conveying the Purpose 98

Word Choice Selecting Striking
Words and Phrases 106

UNIT 5 Expository 115

Sentence Fluency Varying Sentence Types......................... 116

Ideas Developing the Topic 124

Organization Structuring the Body 132

Week

1

The Writing Process

Week

2

Prewriting

Focus Traits
Ideas, Organization, and Voice

Week

3

Drafting

Focus Traits
Word Choice and Sentence Fluency

Week

4

Revising

Focus Traits
Ideas, Organization, Voice, Word Choice, and Sentence Fluency

Week

5

Editing

Focus Traits
Conventions and Presentation

Getting Started

The writing traits are the language you use with your teacher and classmates to talk about what good writing looks like. The traits are

- **Ideas**
- **Organization**
- **Voice**
- **Word Choice**
- **Sentence Fluency**
- **Conventions**
- **Presentation**

You'll learn more about each trait in the weeks to come. You'll also learn how to use the traits in your own writing as you prewrite, draft, revise, edit, and publish. What makes the traits so great? They help YOU be a great writer!

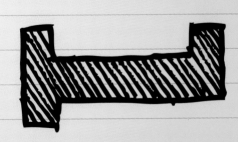

Steps in the Writing Process

The Writing Process and the Writing Traits

Think of the writing process as steps that lead you to choices you make as a writer. You can spend a lot of time on each one or just a little, and you can follow them in order or go back to one to create a better piece.

When you use the writing process, you talk and think about your writing. That's where the traits come in. The traits are the words and vocabulary you use to describe good writing and to check your writing to make sure it is the best it can be. The writing process and the traits go hand in hand.

The Writing Process and Me

The step in the writing process that I think will be the easiest for me is _____

_____

because _____

_____

_____

_____

_____

The step in the writing process that I think will be the most challenging for me is _____

_____

because _____

_____

_____

_____

_____

Meet the Trait Mates

Draw your own versions of the trait icons in the circles, and add a short definition of the trait underneath each.

The Trait Mates are here. Write on, dudes!

I Have a Talent

Write about a talent that you have.

The Writing Process

Home Sweet Giant's Home

Now that you've read *Hewitt Anderson's Great Big Life*, choose five everyday household objects that you might find in a giant's house and describe them in detail. Just how big are they? How and why are they useful to a giant? Use your imagination. Provide sketches if you wish.

Object 1:

_____

_____

Object 2:

_____

_____

Object 3:

_____

_____

Object 4:

_____

_____

Object 5:

_____

_____

I Am a Writer

Use cutout letters from magazines to write a sentence about something you do well in writing—it can be big (I have great ideas.) or important (I always try my hardest.) or small (Wait! There are no small ideas about writing!). Tape or paste them here.

Steps in the Writing Process

Prewriting

When you prewrite, you decide on the purpose and main topic for your writing. You also think about how to organize your ideas and how your piece should sound. Prewriting allows you to explore the possibilities and gives you a place to begin.

What Writers Think About As They Prewrite

Here are six techniques for prewriting. Match each one to an example of what a writer might think about when applying it. Write the correct number in the blank.

Prewriting Techniques

1. **Reading**
   Read books, magazines, and information on the Web.

2. **Using a Journal**
   Record wonderings and experiences and use them in writing.

3. **Talking**
   Discuss topics with other writers, ask questions, contact experts.

4. **Summarizing**
   Write down what you know about a topic to see what else you need.

5. **Creating a Story Map**
   Fill in details about story elements before beginning the piece.

6. **Listening as a Writer**
   Listen to people, places, and things with a "writer's ear."

Examples

___ When the weatherman visits my class today, I'd like to ask why we've had so many tornadoes lately.

___ This news article explains why Amelia Earhart was an incredible American. She did ___ and ___ and ___.

___ I wonder what it would be like to trade places with the president for a day. Good and bad, I bet.

___ Tsunamis fascinate me. I'm going to check out websites that provide information about them.

___ I heard a woman say, "I have 12 cats!" I wonder how much cat food they would eat in a day? Yikes!

___ I've got this idea about an alien space invasion. I need to plan it out so it goes in the right order.

Uh, no. Prewriting does not mean two hours of video games before you write.

Prewriting Technique Sheet

Animal _____

Prewriting Technique _____

_____

_____

_____

_____

_____

_____

_____

_____

_____

_____

_____

_____

_____

_____

_____

_____

_____

An Admirable American

Write about an American who has inspired *you*.

1. Prewrite

_____

_____

_____

_____

_____

_____

2. Draft (three minutes)

_____

_____

_____

_____

_____

_____

This is a *quack*-tastic topic!

Prewriting Partner Interview

My Topic: _____

My Prewriting Technique: _____

Question 1: _____

_____

Response: _____

_____

Question 2: _____

_____

Response: _____

_____

Question 3: _____

_____

Response: _____

_____

Question 4: _____

_____

Response: _____

_____

[Think About: **Prewriting**]

☐ Did I establish a purpose for my writing and decide on the best way to communicate it?

☐ Did I gather key information about my topic?

☐ Did I consider the audience for my writing, so my choice of voice is appropriate?

☐ Did I talk to someone, read a book or Web article, create a story map, listen as a writer, summarize, and/or use my journal to brainstorm my thoughts about this topic?

Where do smart spiders find a strong idea?

Duh! On the web, of course!

Ideas

Presentation

Steps in the Writing Process

Prewriting → Drafting → Revising → Editing → Finishing/Publishing

Drafting

You've come up with some original and intriguing ideas in prewriting. To help get started, think about the lead, the details, and who will read the piece. The rest will come more easily once those things are clear. Remember, you're working on a rough draft, not a finished piece. You just need to get the piece moving.

What Writers Think About As They Draft

Writers draft to explore their topic on paper. They might create a quick lead and ending for the piece, and sketch out the main ideas in between. They begin to establish their voice—and think about word choice and sentence fluency, too. But their priority is to capture their ideas.

Tarantula

I was in the desert with my parents. We were driving along the back roads near my grandfathers house. We saw a dark spot in the road

Dad stopped. It was a tarantula. I had never see one before. I asked Dad what we should do.

Dad said the tarantula was harmliss. "It's part of the balence of life in the desert, he said.

I told him that we should get out of their before it make our car its home.

Terrific topic!

Now the writer needs to spin it into something spectacular.

Drafting

Snags in the Drafting Process

Sometimes I run into trouble during the drafting process because I worry about...

my spelling

whether I have said enough

whether I have enough information

where I should speed up or slow down

how to begin

how to end

whether I've used enough strong verbs

the best way to say something

whether my sentences begin too much the same way

my punctuation

giving my reader what he or she needs to know

knowing whether my piece is boring or interesting

Disaster!

Every day, things happen in our world that are truly terrifying—hurricanes, floods, earthquakes, tornadoes. Write about a natural disaster you have experienced, read about, or seen on TV.

_____

_____

_____

_____

_____

_____

_____

_____

_____

_____

Avoid a writing disaster! Use vivid verbs, nimble nouns, and *ph*-abulous phrases!

Drafting

My 50-Word Sentence

Write a 50-word sentence of thanks to Ojiisan for saving the villagers in *Tsunami!*

_____ _____ _____ _____ _____ (5)

_____ _____ _____ _____ _____ (10)

_____ _____ _____ _____ _____ (15)

_____ _____ _____ _____ _____ (20)

_____ _____ _____ _____ _____ (25)

_____ _____ _____ _____ _____ (30)

_____ _____ _____ _____ _____ (35)

_____ _____ _____ _____ _____ (40)

_____ _____ _____ _____ _____ (45)

_____ _____ _____ _____ _____ (50)

No "ands" and "buts" about it—hold onto your Traits, Mates!

[Think About: **Drafting**]

☐ Did I use my prewriting ideas to drive my drafting decisions?

☐ Did I include a quick lead, a good start on the body of my piece, and a brief ending?

☐ Did I let my ideas flow, knowing I can revise for accuracy later?

☐ Did I put some thought into word choice and sentence fluency?

My 5-Word Sentence

Revise your 50-word thank-you sentence to Ojiisan, by reducing it to only five words.

_____ _____ _____

_____ _____

Check. Check. Quack. Check. Check.

Voice

Steps in the Writing Process

Prewriting → Drafting → Revising → Editing → Finishing/Publishing

Revising

When you revise, you make changes to your writing so it is as clear as it can be. You reread your draft and rework it until it is just right for the reader. Save any worries about conventions until the editing stage. Revising often begins with sharing your piece with someone else. Then you can use the traits to polish it up and make it shine!

What Writers Think About As They Revise

Here are some questions writers think about when they revise. Ask yourself these when you revise your drafts.

Ideas

- Is my topic focused and developed?
- Have I included specific, interesting, and accurate details?
- Have I shared some new thinking about the topic?

Organization

- Have I created a distinct lead, body, and ending?
- Do my details unfold in a logical order?
- Does the structure make my piece a pleasure to read?

Voice

- Do I have my audience and purpose clearly in mind?
- Do I present my ideas in an original way?
- Can the reader "hear" my voice in the writing?

Word Choice

- Are my words accurate, specific, and natural-sounding?
- Do my words show that I have a powerful vocabulary?
- Have I painted a picture with my words?

Sentence Fluency

- Have I presented a variety of well-built sentences?
- Have I woven my sentences together so that they flow?
- Does my writing invite expressive oral reading?

Revising is a time to spice it up. Some salt, pepper, and a few transition words will help.

Now you're cooking!

What's for dessert?

Revising

Tame the Tarantula!

These sentences about deadly creatures have no pizzazz. Revise them to make them roar with excitement! Add sentences, if you wish.

1. A tarantula is a hairy spider.

   _____

   _____

2. The tarantula grabbed the insect to eat.

   _____

   _____

3. The black mamba is a scary snake.

   _____

   _____

4. The wolf ran through the forest to catch the rabbit.

   _____

   _____

5. A big bear was seen near the campsite.

   _____

   _____

When I revise, I can make my writing stronger by...

Just One Suitcase

If you had just one suitcase in which to pack your most treasured items not purchased in a store, what would you pack and why?

Where are my bananas? I know I packed them!

Even Great Inventors Revise: The Wright Brothers

Fill in the chart using information from the drawings on "Four Wright Aircraft."

Description of Aircraft (earliest to latest)	Wingspan	Year Built

How were the Wright Brothers' revisions to their aircraft like revisions you make to your writing?

[Think About: **Revising**]

☐ Did I use accurate and interesting details to enrich and support my topic?

☐ Did I anticipate and answer the reader's questions?

☐ Did I refine words and sentences so they are precise, colorful, and varied?

☐ Did I start out strong and end just as strong?

When revising, don't forget to wag de-tails!

Steps in the Writing Process

Prewriting → Drafting → Revising → Editing → Finishing/ Publishing

Editing

You edit because you want your reader to have no problem reading what you've written. When you edit, you check your work for spelling, capitalization, punctuation and paragraphing, and grammar and usage. You clean up your writing to follow standard English rules. Editing makes your work in all the other traits shine.

What Writers Think About As They Edit

Conventions are the "rules of the writing road." They guide the reader through your piece by making it easy to read. Here are some questions all writers should think about when they edit.

Spelling

- Did I spell words accurately, using a dictionary if needed?

Capitalization

- Did I use uppercase letters correctly, even in tricky places?

Punctuation

- Did I use punctuation correctly, or purposely use it creatively?

Paragraphing

- Did I indent paragraphs and begin them in the right places?

Grammar and Usage

- Did I follow grammar and usage rules to make my writing clear and understandable?

Mark It Up!

Read carefully and highlight errors you find in this piece.

Tarantula!

I was in the sonoran desert with my parents, driving along the back roads near my grandfathers house. We bumped along slowly. Then up ahead on the unpaved road, we saw a dark spot It looked like it was moving.

Dad stopped, and we looked closer. Yikes! It was a tarantula! I had never see a real tarantula before. "What should we do?" I squealed. "Should we kill it?"

Dad laughed. "No," he said. "we should leave it alone. It's pretty harmliss. It could bite in self-defense, and those long hairs on its body can be irritating—but it's more afraid of us than we are of it. Besides, it's part of the balence of life in the desert.

I rolled my eyes. "I know it has a place in nature," I said. "But let's get out of hear before it think that place is in our car!"

[Think About: **Editing**]

☐ Did I check my spelling one word at a time and look up words if needed?

☐ Did I add correct punctuation and start paragraphs in the right places?

☐ Did I use uppercase letters correctly?

☐ Did I apply standard English grammar and usage?

UsInG cApItAls correctly and sppeling write is immpoortint!

Oh, my! Edit yourself, please.

Presentation

Conventions

Tips for Computer Editing

Tools to Edit for Conventions

insert	Use me to add letters, words, phrases, or sentences.
delete	Want to remove unwanted letters, words, phrases, or sentences? Try me.
find and replace	Need to search to find a specific word or phrase that you want to replace? I'm your tool.
cut, copy, and paste	Need to highlight text to cut or copy and paste elsewhere? Use me.
undo	Oops! It's easy to undo something and return to your previous version.
check spelling	Don't forget to turn on the spell-check function so that misspelled words will be underlined in red. Check the list of possible substitutions.

Tools to Edit for Presentation

change font	Want your piece to stand out? Select the best, most readable font for your document. You can even choose a fancy font for your title.
change style (boldface, underline, italic, size, case, bullets)	It's fun to <u>underline</u> text or make it **bold** or *italic*. You can also change the size of a word or make lowercase letters all UPPERCASE. Don't forget to use bullets to make lists easier to read.
change color	WOW! You can really make words pop or call attention to them by using color.
change line spacing	Text too heavy to read? Change the spacing between the lines to help out.
insert art or graphics	Need to add a picture or chart? Use clip art or your own pictures to jazz up your piece!
check spelling	Don't forget to turn on the spell-check function so that misspelled words will be underlined in red. Check the list of possible substitutions.

Rate the Papers

Here are two examples of expository writing.
Which paper is stronger? Why do you think so?

Paper 1

My special place is a fort in the woods. I like to go there with my friends. The woods are a good place to play and to enjoy nature. We splash in the water and hide from each other. We have hours and hours of fun in the woods. It's so relaxing to be away from everything else but the woods and hanging out with my friends. They like the woods as much as me. We go there as often as we can.

Paper 2

Crash! We run across rocks. Racing through the yard towards the woods, closer to our secret place. I see my two best buds next to me, feel that crisp, cool breeze against my face mixed with the hot summer air and all those good feelings running down my spine. I feel happy and free, like I could run forever.

The sun is bearing down on us as we crash through the opening in the woods. No one wants to stop, but run forever. We smell the wonderful oak trees and feel the hard crackling twigs beneath my tennis shoes. Nothing else matters but crashing through the woods with my buddies. I hear the foot the footsteps of my buds and me crashing and dodging around, the comforting laughter of each other.

With the sun shining through the trees we can clearly see the fort nearing closer and closer. Feeling that whisking wind against my skin and knowing the fort is close urges us to run until we collapse in the fort. And then we are there. We feel the fresh, crisp dirt as we lay in it. We are finally there and let the good feeling rush over us as we sit in the comfort of the fort.

Editing

Editing Marks

Mark	Meaning	Example
℘	Delete material.	The writing is is good.
sp	Correct the spelling or spell it out.	We are exploring ②traits this weak.
∩	Close space.	To day is publishing day.
∧	Insert a letter, word, or phrase.	My teacher has books. wonderful
℘	Change a letter.	She is a great wroter.
⧣	Add a space.	Don't forget astrong lead.
∿	Transpose letters or words.	She roed the piece with flair!
≡	Change to a capital letter.	We have j. k. Rowling to thank for Harry Potter's magic.
/	Change to a lowercase letter.	"A Writer's work is never Done" was his favorite saying.
¶	Start a new paragraph.	"What day is it?" he inquired. "It's National Writing Day," she replied.
⊙	Add a period.	Think about all the traits as you write⊙

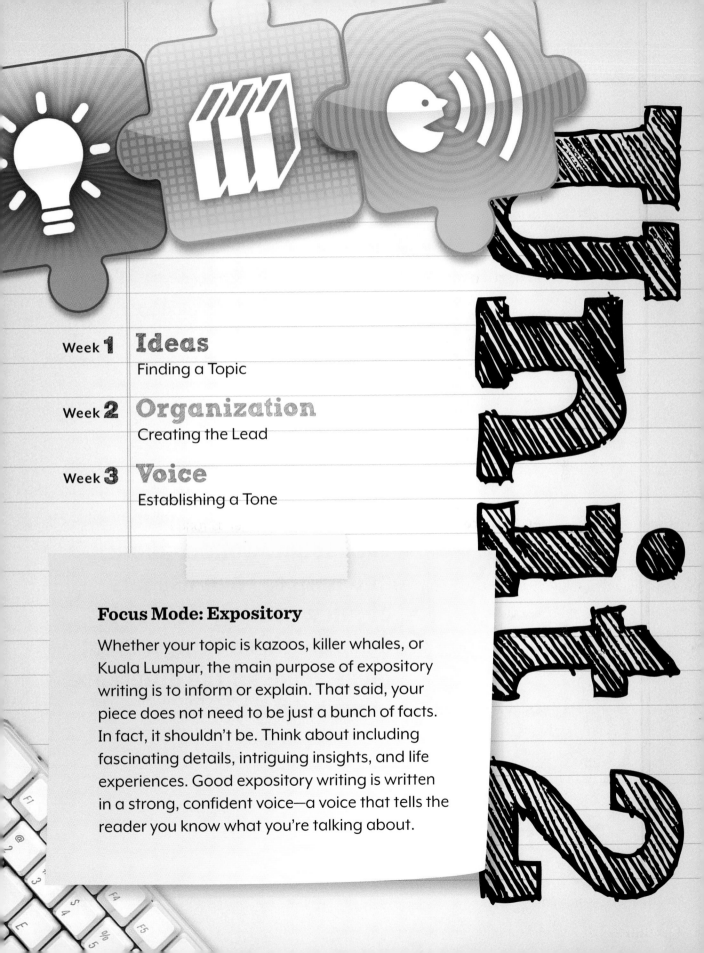

Week **1** **Ideas**
Finding a Topic

Week **2** **Organization**
Creating the Lead

Week **3** **Voice**
Establishing a Tone

Focus Mode: Expository

Whether your topic is kazoos, killer whales, or Kuala Lumpur, the main purpose of expository writing is to inform or explain. That said, your piece does not need to be just a bunch of facts. In fact, it shouldn't be. Think about including fascinating details, intriguing insights, and life experiences. Good expository writing is written in a strong, confident voice—a voice that tells the reader you know what you're talking about.

- **Finding a Topic** ···
- Focusing the Topic
- Developing the Topic
- Using Details

Focus Mode: Expository

Ideas

66 Write about things you care about, wonder about, and notice. Then use lots of juicy, sensory details to describe those things. Great ideas make all the difference in writing! 99

Finding a Topic

Topics are all around you—in things you experience every day. When you find the perfect topic, you know what to say. You see the "big picture." To find the perfect topic, think about what matters to you and write about it so the reader understands why.

How is getting involved in your favorite activities like finding an exciting topic to write about?

Idea Bank

Write down ideas for writing as they occur to you, and you'll have a whole bank of topics. These sentence starters will get the juices flowing.

Now write some ideas on the bills below.

Warm-Up 1

How clear is the topic of this paragraph?

Some dogs have a hard time staying home; they like to roam. Washing your dog correctly keeps your pet clean and healthy. Would you rather have a cat or a dog as a pet?

Revise the paragraph here or on a separate sheet.

This paragraph is a dog!

I beg your pardon?!

Think About

- Have I chosen a topic I really like?
- Do I have something new to say about this topic?
- Am I writing about what I know and care about?
- Have I gathered enough information so that I'm ready to write?

Preview

A Contest Writer

In the spaces below, write about what you think a contest writer does, where you might find writing by a contest writer, and questions you have about the job.

1. A contest writer must have to think several steps ahead. What do you think he or she does first to start developing the rules and guidelines for a contest?

_____

_____

_____

_____

_____

2. Where I have seen—or might see—pieces a contest writer has written:

_____

_____

_____

_____

_____

3. What might be the main challenges of the job:

_____

_____

_____

_____

_____

Write-On Sheet

[Focus on Punctuation]

Write two sentences that contain correct use of apostrophes in plural possessives.

1. _____

_____

_____

2. _____

_____

_____

> 66 The first step to becoming a better writer is believing your own experience is worth writing about. 99
>
> —Peter Marmorek

[Ideas Doodle]

In the space below, create a doodle for the word *ideas*. Think about where writers find ideas and what they do once they have them.

Write a statement that explains your doodle. Share your statement with a classmate and revise it based on any good advice he or she gives you.

_____

_____

_____

_____

_____

Draw a final version of your doodle on a separate sheet of paper and write your statement beneath it. Make sure they are "contest quality."

Suddenly I'm in the mood for some chicken doodle soup!

- **Creating the Lead** ·······························
- Using Sequence Words and Transition Words
- Structuring the Body
- Ending With a Sense of Resolution

Focus Mode: Expository

Organization

"Organization is about the structure of a piece of writing. Nothing holds your piece together—or holds a reader's attention—better than sturdy, easy-to-follow organization."

Creating the Lead

The lead is the beginning of a piece of writing—its first lines. A strong lead grabs the reader's attention. It gives the reader something to think about so that he or she wants to keep reading to find out what you have to say.

How is hooking a fish on a line similar to grabbing your reader's attention?

Techniques for a Strong Start

A great lead makes your reader sit up and pay attention. Here are seven techniques for writing a great lead.

Start the Action

The writer makes something happen.

Example: "I'm off duty," Mom said. "You'll have to make your own sandwich."

Single Word

The writer starts with a stand-alone word and follows it with more information.

Example: Peanut butter! This sticky stuff makes any sandwich delicious.

Fascinating Fact

The writer presents an intriguing piece of information.

Example: According to the National Peanut Board, the average American eats more than six pounds of peanuts and peanut butter products each year.

Imagine This

The writer captures a moment in words or pictures.

Example: It's 3:00 and your tummy is growling.

Compare It

The writer looks at the topic in different ways.

Example: Most people eat peanut butter on bread, but I like it straight from the jar.

Listen Up

The writer describes a sound.

Example: Chomp, smack, crunch.

Question It

The writer asks a question or a series of questions.

Example: What is your favorite kind of sandwich? Have you ever tried peanut butter and pickles?

Warm-Up 2

Dive into this paragraph and give it a splashy lead!

How strong is this paragraph's lead?

You have to bring stuff with you when you go to the pool. It's bad if you forget something. I am going to tell you what to bring with you.

Revise the paragraph here or on a separate sheet.

Think About

- Did I give the reader something interesting to think about right from the start?

- Will the reader want to keep reading?

- Have I tried to get the reader's attention?

- Did I let the reader know what is coming?

Preview

Ben Hillman, author of *How Big Is It?*

Find a partner, discuss the questions below, and answer two of them.

1. Anyone can use numbers to describe size. But Ben Hillman goes one step further by using photographs to compare gigantic objects and animals to ordinary things. How do you think his approach helps readers understand just how big things are?

   _____

   _____

   _____

2. In addition to working as an author of books, Hillman has worked as an animator, filmmaker, and even a designer and painter of a life-sized dinosaur mural in a museum. How do you think these jobs have helped him in his career as an author?

   _____

   _____

   _____

3. Ben Hillman also wrote and illustrated *How Strong Is It?*, *How Fast Is It?*, and *How Weird Is It?* Each of these books combines humor, science, and visual comparisons. What topic do you think Ben Hillman should tackle next? Why?

   _____

   _____

   _____

Write-On Sheet

[My Spelling Words]

List your nine spelling words for the week here.

1.
2.
3.
4.
5.
6.
7.
8.
9.

> **"**If you start with a bang, you won't end with a whimper. **"**
>
> –T. S. Eliot

[Lively Leads Chart]

Listen to the section leads in *How Big Is It?* Record Ben Hillman's leads in the correct box below. Then rewrite one of them on a separate sheet of paper, using another technique.

Time to sniff out some awesome leads!

Start the Action

Example:

Single Word

Example:

Fascinating Fact

Example:

Imagine This

Example:

Compare It

Example:

Listen Up

Example:

Question It

Example:

- **Establishing a Tone** ....
- Conveying the Purpose
- Creating a Connection to the Audience
- Taking Risks to Create Voice

Focus Mode: Expository

Voice

Voice

66 Voice is how you speak to readers. It's how you connect to them and show how much you care about your main idea, whether you're writing fiction or nonfiction. It's the energy in your writing. 99

Establishing a Tone

When you talk, you express how you feel by your body language and the sound, or tone, of your voice. When you write, you express how you feel by the tone of the words you choose. The right tone lets readers know how you feel about the topic and how you want them to feel about it.

How is the tone of a piece of writing like the expression on a person's face?

Voice: **Establishing a Tone**

Tuning In on Tone

With a partner, read each tone descriptor below, decide whether it is upbeat or downbeat, and write it in the appropriate column.

angry, hopeful, excited, anxious, lonely, nervous, relieved, loving, concerned, frustrated, proud

Upbeat	Downbeat

Identify the tone in the following two passages. Which words and phrases helped you determine the tone?

I can't believe people don't recycle. I mean really, like it takes two seconds to put a can in the correct bin and I still see people just tossing them into the trash or leaving them on a table. Don't people care about our planet? They should. It's really important.

Tone: _____

Yesterday, I saw someone toss his can into the trash instead of into the recycling bin. People may not know the benefits of recycling—all the benefits—so maybe this person didn't realize the impact of his actions. I believe we could accomplish great things if everyone recycled. We need to band together and make sure everyone knows the benefits.

Tone: _____

Warm-Up 3

Liberate this paragraph from its *oh-so-boring* voice. Give it a tone of your own!

How is the tone of this paragraph?

The Statue of Liberty is in New York Harbor. It was a gift from France. It's important to many people.

Revise the paragraph here or on a separate sheet.

Think About

- Can I name the primary voice of my writing (for example: happy, upset, wise, scared)?
- Have I changed the tone from the beginning to the end?
- Have I shown how I feel?
- Did I show that I care about this topic?

Preview

Trudee Romanek, author of *Achoo! The Most Interesting Book You'll Ever Read About Germs*

With a partner, read the information about Trudee Romanek online and answer two of the questions below.

1. Read the titles of the books Trudee Romanek has written. What kinds of things do you think she is interested in?

_____

_____

_____

2. What are some words in the titles of Romanek's books that give you a clue about the tone of those books?

_____

_____

_____

3. Think about the titles of the books that Romanek has written. What does she like to do that has become part of the books she writes?

_____

_____

_____

4. Which of Romanek's books grabbed your attention most? Write down the title and what interests you about it.

_____

_____

_____

Write-On Sheet

[Focus on Capitalization]

Write a sentence with proper names capitalized correctly and a sentence with words emphasized in capital letters.

1. _____

_____

_____

2. _____

_____

_____

> 66 Good writing is supposed to evoke sensation in the reader—not the fact that it is raining, but the feeling of being rained upon. 99
>
> —E. L. Doctorow

[Achoo! Graphic Organizer]

Trudee Romanek makes germs fascinating by writing about them in a lively tone. Write down three words and three facts that help convey the tone of *Achoo!*

Even when you're sneezin' you need to be pleasin'. Cough up that perfect tone.

Voice

Germ Words

Fun Germ Facts

[Expository Publishing Checklist]

Think you are ready to go public with your expository unit project? Use this form to make sure you've covered all the writing bases.

I remembered to

☐ include facts and information that came from reliable sources.

☐ weave in details that show how much I know about my topic.

☐ develop the topic logically from beginning to end.

☐ use a voice that expresses my fascination for the topic.

☐ explain any unusual words, phrases, or concepts.

☐ read my piece aloud to check how it will sound to the readers.

☐ proofread my piece carefully and clean up problems with conventions.

Check. Check. Gobble-Gobble. (Oops, wrong bird!) Quack. Check.

Voice

The purpose of my piece is

_____

_____

The part that works the best is

_____

_____

What I hope readers will take away from my piece is

_____

_____

Week 1 **Word Choice**
Applying Strong Verbs

Week 2 **Sentence Fluency**
Crafting Well-Built Sentences

Week 3 **Ideas**
Focusing the Topic

Focus Mode: Narrative

Whether you're writing about a day at wizard camp or a day at your local water park, the main purpose of narrative writing is to tell a story. Your narrative pieces should include characters, a setting, events, a problem to be solved—and maybe a surprise or two. They should capture your reader's interest and hang onto it, right to the end.

- **Applying Strong Verbs** ....
- Selecting Striking Words and Phrases
- Using Specific and Accurate Words
- Choosing Words That Deepen Meaning

Focus Mode: Narrative

Word Choice

Word Choice

66 Using the right words allows you to show what is happening in your piece or what matters to you about your topic. Precise and accurate words help make your main idea stand out. 99

Applying Strong Verbs

You can play a drum or you can *beat* a drum. You can get into a pool or you can *plunge* into a pool. Which would you rather do? Strong verbs pack a punch. They capture action precisely in just one little word. When you use strong verbs, your writing is electrifying. It bursts with energy!

How are a lightning bolt and a strong verb similar?

Animal Actions

Write down strong verbs that describe how each animal moves and acts.

Sharks

- how they move

_____

_____

_____

- how they eat

_____

_____

_____

Lions

- how they move

_____

_____

_____

- how they make noise

_____

_____

_____

Snakes

- how they move

_____

_____

_____

- how they capture their prey

_____

_____

_____

Eagles

- how they move

_____

_____

_____

- how they care for their young

_____

_____

_____

Warm-Up 4

Don't let boring verbs "derail" your writing!

How's this paragraph's verbs?

I am going to see my grandmother. It is going to be fun to go on the train and be with her. She tells good stories.

Revise the paragraph here or on a separate sheet.

Think About

- Have I used action words?

- Did I stretch to get a better word—*scurry* rather than *run*?

- Do my verbs give my writing punch and pizzazz?

- Did I avoid *is, am, was, were, be, being,* and *been* whenever I could?

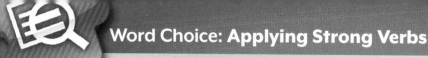

Preview

Ann Herbert Scott, **author of**

Brave as a Mountain Lion

Read the information below and answer two of the questions with a partner.

Her experiences living in Nevada have inspired many of Ann Herbert Scott's books. For example, the main character in *Brave as a Mountain Lion* is based on a boy she met there who was worried about participating in a spelling bee. He was afraid to stand up in front of an audience. Although ideas may seem to come easily to her, Ann Herbert Scott works hard to choose just the right ones for her books. She also works hard to polish her writing. She often reworks a manuscript 20 to 30 times before she considers it finished!

1. Why do you think Ann Herbert Scott chose the simile "brave as a mountain lion" for her title? What other comparison could she have made to capture the idea of bravery?

   _____

   _____

   _____

   _____

2. Think about what you know so far about *Brave as a Mountain Lion*. What are some strong verbs that might work in the story? Explain why.

   _____

   _____

   _____

   _____

3. Why do you think Scott reworks her manuscripts so many times? What kinds of changes do you think she makes?

   _____

   _____

   _____

   _____

Write-On Sheet

[My Spelling Words]

List your nine spelling words for the week here.

1.

2.

3.

4.

5.

6.

7.

8.

9.

> 66 The faster I write the better my output. If I'm going slow, I'm in trouble. It means I'm pushing the words instead of being pulled by them. 99
>
> —Raymond Chandler

[Vigorous Verbs Roar]

Ann Herbert Scott knows how to apply strong verbs. Here are a few from *Brave as a Mountain Lion*. Use each one in a sentence.

1. **stomping**

   _____

2. **stretched**

   _____

3. **shoved**

   _____

4. **repeated**

   _____

5. **whispered**

   _____

6. **peeked**

   _____

7. **scraped**

   _____

8. **slipped**

   _____

9. **dangling**

   _____

10. **glistened**

    _____

These verbs do ROAR. They're purr-fect!

- **Crafting Well-Built Sentences** ·················
- Varying Sentence Types
- Capturing Smooth and Rhythmic Flow
- Breaking the "Rules" to Create Fluency

Focus Mode: Narrative

Sentence Fluency

Sentence Fluency

"To create sentence fluency, you have to read with your ears *and* eyes. Make your writing sound as good as it looks by building sentences that flow smoothly from one to the next. "

Crafting Well-Built Sentences

What does it mean for a piece of writing to have well-built sentences? It means the sentences are not all short or all long. They start with different words, not the same word over and over again. Words like *but*, *and*, and *so* join sentence parts. Well-built sentences move the reader through the piece.

How are the sentences in a piece of writing like the materials that were used to construct this building?

What Happened?

Reorganize each group of words into a well-built sentence. Don't forget uppercase letters and punctuation marks!

1. hyenas closed in / an impala / and chased the leopard away / soon after a leopard caught

_____

_____

_____

2. while the hyenas feasted / not far away / from the tall grass / on her catch / the leopard watched

_____

_____

_____

3. a shady place / stuffed / the hyenas wandered off / to find water and / to nap

_____

_____

_____

4. up a tree / just before / and safely dragged her carcass / the leopard crept back / one hyena returned

_____

_____

_____

Warm-Up 5

This paragraph needs more than a better diet. It needs a sentence fluency workout!

Are the sentences in this paragraph well built?

Pat, Sue, and I exercise. We exercise every day. We go to a gym. All of our teachers have classes. They are good. Exercise makes the body of every person stronger. We know ours are.

Revise the paragraph here or on a separate sheet.

Think About

- Do my sentences begin in different ways?
- Are my sentences of different lengths?
- Are my sentences grammatically correct (unless I broke rules for impact)?
- Have I used conjunctions such as *but, and,* and *so* to turn shorter sentences into longer ones?

Sentence Fluency: **Crafting Well-Built Sentences**

Lois Lowry, author of *Crow Call*

**Find a partner, discuss the questions below, and answer
two of them.**

1. *Crow Call* is about a special day Lois Lowry spent with her father after he returned from World War II. Why do you think she chose to focus on the events of only one day?

_____

_____

_____

_____

_____

2. Lowry says that the sights, sounds, and even smells of her childhood are always an important part of the books she writes. How can using memories of sensory experiences help you as a writer, too?

_____

_____

_____

_____

_____

3. Lois Lowry says that she loves "the process of finding the right rhythm of words, then putting it all together." How does this relate to sentence fluency?

_____

_____

_____

_____

_____

Write-On Sheet

[Focus on Grammar and Usage]

Write one sentence that includes a plural possessive noun.

1. _____

_____

Write one sentence that includes a plural possessive pronoun.

2. _____

_____

> 66 Do not worry.... All you have to do is write one true sentence. Write the truest sentence that you know. 99
>
> —Ernest Hemingway

[Looking at *Crow Call*]

Read a page from *Crow Call* and answer these questions about its sentences. For each question, write an example from the *Crow Call* page.

Do the sentences begin in different ways?	
Are the sentences different lengths?	
Are the sentences grammatically correct? If not, are grammar rules broken for creative reasons?	
Does the author use conjunctions such as _but_, _and_, and _so_ to connect sentence parts?	

Below, write down one of your favorite sentences from the book and explain why you like it so much.

I think *Rabbit Call* would make a beautiful story, too. Where's my book agent?

- Finding a Topic
- **Focusing the Topic** ··················
- Developing the Topic
- Using Details

Focus Mode: Narrative

Ideas

"Write about things you care about, wonder about, and notice. Then use lots of juicy, sensory details to describe those things. Great ideas make all the difference in writing!"

Focusing the Topic

When you focus your topic, you zero in on something important or interesting about it. You make your writing clear and strong because you're not taking on the whole world—you're taking on one really cool corner of it.

How is getting a clear image of something under a microscope like focusing your topic for writing?

Ideas: **Focusing the Topic**

Zeroing In on the Forest

You're parachuting into the forest. Answer these questions to zero in on what you see.

1. Imagine flying over a forest. Look down. What do you see?

   _____

   _____

2. Fly a little lower over part of the forest. What do you see?

   _____

   _____

3. Parachute in. You're still airborne. What are three things you see in the part of the forest you're headed toward?

   _____

   _____

4. Focus on one of those things. What is it?

   _____

5. Look closer at it. What can you say about its size, shape, color?

   _____

   _____

6. Why is it important to the forest?

   _____

   _____

7. How does it make you feel? What do you want to tell others about it?

   _____

   _____

   _____

Warm-Up 6

Is the topic of this paragraph focused?

I'm right at home with this topic!

Ideas

The news article explained the role of rain forests in our environment. There are rain forests in many places. I went to a science museum that has a rain forest exhibit. The rain forests are disappearing at an alarming rate.

Revise the paragraph here or on a separate sheet.

Think About

- Have I zeroed in on one small part of a bigger idea?

- Can I sum up my idea in a simple sentence?

- Have I chosen the information that best captures my idea?

- Have I thought deeply about what the reader will need to know?

Ideas: **Focusing the Topic**

A Historian

In the spaces below, write down what you think a historian does, where you might find a historian's work, and questions you have about the job.

1. A historian may be able to study old documents and artifacts before writing about historical events. What do you think might be most interesting about being a historian?

_____

_____

_____

_____

_____

2. Where do you think you might see—or may already have seen—a historian's work?

_____

_____

_____

_____

_____

3. Do you think the job of a historian could ever be frustrating or boring? Explain what might be the downside of this profession.

_____

_____

_____

_____

_____

Write-On Sheet

[My Spelling Words]

List your nine spelling words for the week here.

1.

2.

3.

4.

5.

6.

7.

8.

9.

> 66 You cannot depend on your eyes when your imagination is out of focus. 99
>
> —Mark Twain

[A Magnificent Monument Plaque]

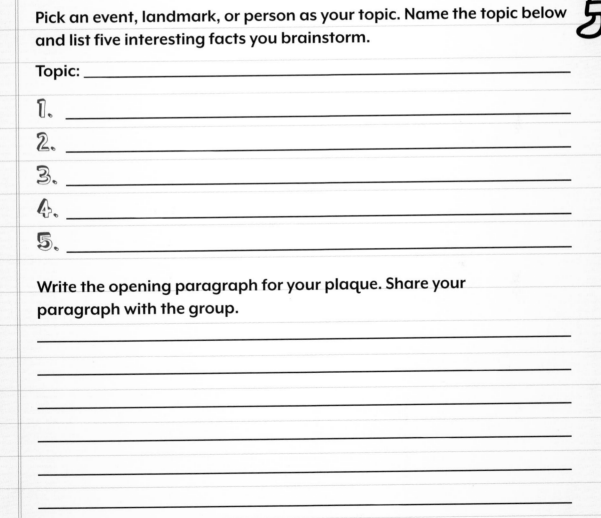

Plaque? No way! I always floss before brushing.

Create a monument plaque for one of these categories:

1. A historical event, such as the first airplane flight or the discovery of penicillin

2. A historical landmark, such as the United States Naval Base at Pearl Harbor, Hawaii, or the Liberty Bell, in Philadelphia

3. A famous person from history, such as Frederick Douglass, Clara Barton, or John Glenn

Pick an event, landmark, or person as your topic. Name the topic below and list five interesting facts you brainstorm.

Topic: _____

1. _____

2. _____

3. _____

4. _____

5. _____

Write the opening paragraph for your plaque. Share your paragraph with the group.

_____

_____

_____

_____

_____

_____

[Narrative Publishing Checklist]

Think you are ready to go public with your narrative unit project? Use this form to make sure you've covered all the writing bases.

I remembered to

- develop a fascinating story line with interesting characters.

- include a time and place that work well with the story line.

- present a problem and a solution.

- give the story a clear beginning, middle, and end.

- use an active voice to entertain, surprise, and challenge the reader.

- choose words that enhance the characters, time, and place.

- read my piece aloud to check how it will sound to the readers.

- proofread my piece carefully and clean up problems with conventions.

The purpose of my piece is

_____

My favorite part is

_____

What I hope readers will find most memorable about my piece is

_____

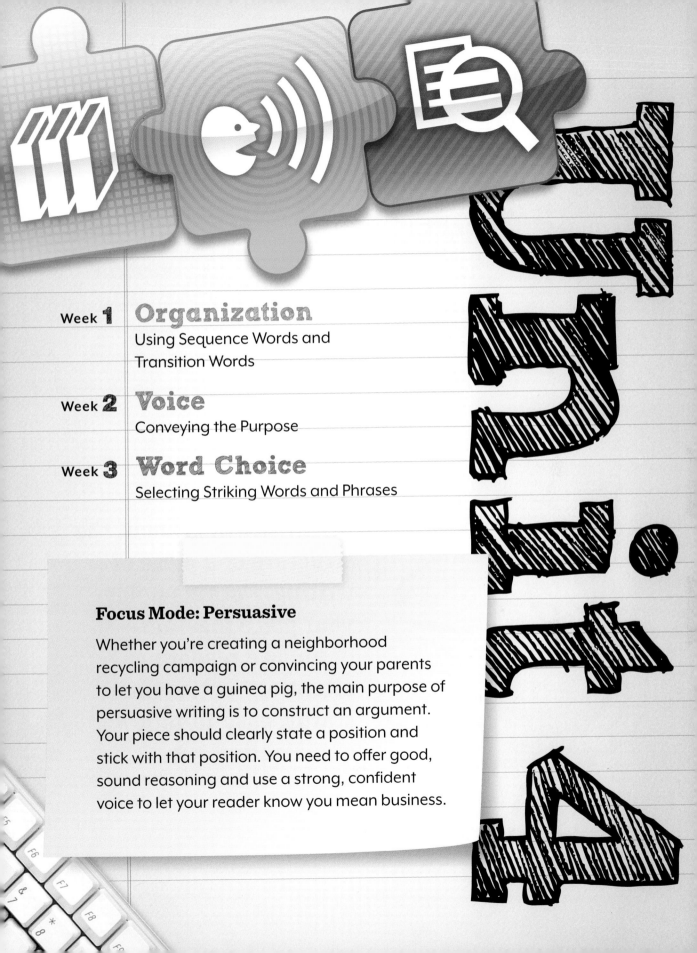

Week 1 **Organization**
Using Sequence Words and
Transition Words

Week 2 **Voice**
Conveying the Purpose

Week 3 **Word Choice**
Selecting Striking Words and Phrases

Focus Mode: Persuasive

Whether you're creating a neighborhood
recycling campaign or convincing your parents
to let you have a guinea pig, the main purpose of
persuasive writing is to construct an argument.
Your piece should clearly state a position and
stick with that position. You need to offer good,
sound reasoning and use a strong, confident
voice to let your reader know you mean business.

- Creating the Lead
- **Using Sequence Words and Transition Words**
- Structuring the Body
- Ending With a Sense of Resolution

Focus Mode: Persuasive

Organization

Organization

❝Organization is about the structure of a piece of writing. Nothing holds your piece together— or holds a reader's attention—better than sturdy, easy-to-follow organization.❞

Using Sequence Words and Transition Words

Sequence words (such as *next* and *finally*) and transition words (such as *but* and *also*) are the links you use to connect your ideas from one sentence to the next. When you use just the right words, your sentences fit together perfectly.

How is using sequence words and transition words like laying out domino tiles?

Sequence Words and Transition Words

There's no better way to connect ideas than by using sequence and transition words. Here are a few examples and reasons to use them.

Purpose	Examples
to identify location or position	over, under, on top of, behind, in front of, next to, around, beside, beneath
	My table is next to my bed and across from the door.
to show a sequence of time	first, next, then, last, finally, while, after that, before, following, during
	You will want to wet your toothbrush first.
to begin or continue a line of thinking	to start, mainly, furthermore, as well as, nevertheless, indeed, certainly, most important, in other words, of course, to be sure
	And, most important, ask for help if you need it.
to sum up	after all, all in all, in conclusion, therefore, in the final analysis, thus
	That's what best friends are for, after all.
to give information	for example, for instance, to illustrate, specifically
	For example, you could mix red paint and yellow paint to make orange.
to compare or contrast	like, also, in the same way, similarly, in contrast, but, instead, however, on the other hand, unlike
	I have blonde hair, like my sister.

Warm-Up 7

With the right linking words, this paragraph could be mighty tasty!

How are the sequence and transition words in this piece?

Jeremiah bakes the best cookies. He mixes butter, sugar, and eggs. He stirs in flour, salt, and baking soda. He adds dark chocolate chips.

What makes Jeremiah's cookies special? Store-bought cookies are crumbly dry. Jeremiah's are warm, fresh, and chewy. They are made with love.

Revise the paragraphs here or on a separate sheet.

Think About

- Did I use sequence words (*later, then, meanwhile*)?
- Did I use transition words (*however, because*, and *also*)?
- Do my ideas connect from sentence to sentence?
- Does my organization make sense from paragraph to paragraph?

Preview

Lynne Truss, author of *Eats, Shoots & Leaves*

Answer two of the questions below. Discuss your answers with a partner.

1. Lynne Truss studied English language and literature in school, writes books and articles and reviews, has been an editor, and has worked in a library. How do you think these jobs might have inspired her to write this book about punctuation?

   _____

   _____

   _____

   _____

2. Truss gave her book a very clever title. Take a close look at the phrase *Eats, Shoots & Leaves*. What does it tell you about pandas? Now, how would the meaning be different if there were no comma after the word *Eats*?

   _____

   _____

   _____

   _____

3. Truss has written books about punctuation and manners, newspaper columns about sports, and short stories. If you met her, what would be the first question you'd ask about her work?

   _____

   _____

   _____

   _____

Write-On Sheet

[Focus on Grammar and Usage]

Write two sentences containing direct objects.

1. _____

   _____

   _____

2. _____

   _____

   _____

66 Have something to say, and say it as clearly as you can. That is the only secret. 99

—Matthew Arnold

[Crossed Connections]

Read the sentences below. Illustrate each one in the spirit of *Eats, Shoots & Leaves.* Use a separate sheet if necessary.

You might want to eat, shoot, and leave some of these sentences!

Want to eat, Kitty?	Want to eat Kitty?
First place, my painting!	First, place my painting.

- Establishing a Tone
- **Conveying the Purpose** ············
- Creating a Connection to the Audience
- Taking Risks to Create Voice

Focus Mode: Persuasive

Voice

Voice

> **"Voice is how you speak to readers. It's how you connect to them and show how much you care about your main idea, whether you're writing fiction or nonfiction. It's the energy in your writing."**

Conveying the Purpose

The voice you use in a piece of writing should match your purpose for writing the piece. If you're writing a letter of thanks, your tone might be appreciative. But if you're writing a letter of complaint, your tone might be stern. Use your voice to convey what you think and how you feel. Don't leave any doubt in your reader's mind.

How is cooking with the right pan like finding just the right voice to get your idea across?

Purposes for Writing

To Inform

Mode: Expository

Possible formats: research reports, how-to essays, news stories

Possible tones: knowledgeable, serious . . .

To Tell a Story

Mode: Narrative

Possible formats: short stories, personal narratives, comic strips

Possible tones: funny, scary, thoughtful . . .

To Construct an Argument

Mode: Persuasive

Possible formats: advertisements, letters of recommendation or complaint, speeches

Possible tones: confident, wise, convincing . . .

Read each statement and write down its purpose.

You'll never guess what happened on the way home from school.

_____

Research has shown that cutting down rain forests is harmful to the atmosphere.

_____

Our sandwiches are so tasty you'll want to eat them for breakfast, lunch, and dinner.

_____

We have rock-bottom prices on new bikes. You won't find a better deal.

_____

Ella squealed when she saw the big package waiting on her doorstep.

_____

Warm-Up 8

Is the writer's purpose for writing this paragraph clear?

Homework stinks. I don't like to do it, especially on the weekends. Don't teachers want to have some free time? I sure do. I'm telling my teachers that I'm not doing homework on the weekends anymore. It's not fair.

Revise the paragraph here or use a separate sheet.

Uh oh! Can you fix this kid's tone before he gets us all in trouble?!

Voice

Think About

- Is the purpose of my writing clear?
- Does my point of view come through?
- Is this the right tone for this kind of writing?
- Have I used strong voice throughout this piece?

Preview

James Cross Giblin, author of

The Many Rides of Paul Revere

Answer two of the questions below. Discuss your answers with a partner.

1. James Cross Giblin was once a children's book editor. What do you think a children's book editor does? How might Giblin's work as an author be similar to or different from his work as an editor?

_____

_____

_____

2. Giblin believes young writers should keep journals. He says that writing a journal is for an author like exercising is for an athlete. How are the two activities alike? Is this good advice? Explain.

_____

_____

_____

3. Some of Giblin's books include *The Amazing Life of Benjamin Franklin; Thomas Jefferson: A Picture Book Biography; Secrets of the Sphinx;* and *A Century That Was: Reflections on the Last One Hundred Years.* Based on the titles, what kinds of things do you think he likes to write about?

_____

_____

_____

4. Which of Giblin's books listed above do you think you would most enjoy reading? Explain your choice.

_____

_____

_____

Write-On Sheet

[My Spelling Words]

List your nine spelling words for the week here.

1.

2.

3.

4.

5.

6.

7.

8.

9.

> " Be yourself. Above all, let who you are, what you are, what you believe shine through every sentence you write, every piece you finish. "
>
> —John Jakes

[What's the Purpose, Patriot?]

Read the writing formats and ideas in the first column. In the second column, write a possible purpose for each one (to inform, to construct an argument, or to tell a story). Then write a sentence that captures an appropriate tone.

Paul Revere rocks! Giddy up, writer!

Idea/ Format: an account of Paul Revere's ride, written from the point of view of his horse

Purpose: _____

Your Sentence: _____

_____

_____

Idea/ Format: a request from Paul Revere's mother urging him not to make the ride

Purpose: _____

Your Sentence: _____

_____

_____

Idea/ Format: a message from Paul Revere himself to the people of Massachusetts, just before the ride

Purpose: _____

Your Sentence: _____

_____

_____

- Applying Strong Verbs
- **Selecting Striking Words and Phrases** ················
- Using Specific and Accurate Words
- Choosing Words That Deepen Meaning

Focus Mode: Persuasive

Word Choice

❝Using the right words allows you to show what is happening in your piece or what matters to you about your topic. Precise and accurate words help make your main idea stand out.❞

Selecting Striking Words and Phrases

Striking words and phrases make your writing sparkle. Readers feel as if they're inside your piece, rather than on the sidelines. Precise, descriptive words and phrases linger in the mind. Readers think about the piece long after they have finished reading it. They think "yum!" not "yawn!"

How is selecting striking words and phrases for your writing like adding spices to your food?

Basic vs. Striking

Write your team's ideas for a striking substitute for each of the basic words. In the last column, write the class winner for each.

Basic Word	Your Team's Idea	Class Winner
go		
nice		
bad		
fun		
good		
like		
make		
said		
walk		

Warm-Up 9

An apple? No way!
This tabby wants tuna.

How striking are the words and phrases in this paragraph?

You don't have to eat bad food after school. Apples are a good snack. They taste good. They are good for you. Eat an apple instead.

Revise the paragraph here or on a separate sheet.

Think About

- Did I try to use words that sound *just right*?
- Did I try hyphenating several shorter words to make an interesting-sounding new word?
- Did I try putting together words with the same sound?
- Did I read my piece aloud to find at least one or two moments I love?

Preview

A Food Writer

In the spaces below, answer the questions about what a food writer does and what makes him or her good at the job.

1. Think of three food products you know so well, you could write a packaging label for them. What words or phrases particularly stick in your mind about each?

_____

_____

_____

_____

_____

2. If someone offered you a job as a food writer, what do you think you'd do all day? What would be evidence that you were good at your job?

_____

_____

_____

_____

_____

3. If you were a food writer, what trait or traits would be most important for you to keep in mind as you write? Why?

_____

_____

_____

_____

_____

Write-On Sheet

[Focus on Grammar and Usage]

Write two sentences that contain a subject and a predicate.
Circle the subject in each sentence. Underline the predicate.

1. _____

_____

_____

2. _____

_____

_____

66 Words are only postage stamps delivering the object for you to unwrap. 99

—George Bernard Shaw

[Super Cereal]

Mice Krispies! They're furry*licious*.

Headline: A bold beginning that grabs buyers' attention and urges them to read on.
Example: *Treat Your Feet to a Walk on Clouds!*

Facts: Information that buyers need to purchase the product with confidence.
Example: *Four layers of cushiony innersole . . .*

Humor: Laughs sell—most of the time—and make buyers feel positive about the product.
Example: *Shoes so comfortable a duck would want them.*

Sensory Images: Words and pictures that appeal to buyers' relationship to the world.
Example: *Walk on air!*

Testimonials: Well-known people who claim they use the product—and encourage buyers to use it, too.
Example: *Volleyball champ Shawna Waite says: "Try them! I know you'll love them!"*

With your classmates, come up with a new brand of cereal and write down striking words and phrases to describe it. Then, on a separate sheet of paper, draft a description for the box, using some of the elements described above.

Cereal Name: _____

Striking Words and Phrases to Describe It: _____

_____

_____

_____

_____

_____

[Persuasive Publishing Checklist]

Think you are ready to go public with your extended persuasive project? Use this form to make sure you've covered all the writing bases.

I remembered to

All right, writers, it's showtime!

- [ ] clearly state my position on the topic and stick with it.

- [ ] offer good, sound reasoning that the reader can relate to easily.

- [ ] provide solid facts, opinions, and examples that are based on reliable, objective sources.

- [ ] expose weaknesses in other positions.

- [ ] develop my argument using solid reasoning from beginning to end.

- [ ] use a compelling, confident voice to add credibility.

- [ ] explain any unusual words, phrases, or concepts.

- [ ] read my piece aloud to check how it will sound to the reader.

- [ ] proofread my piece carefully and clean up problems with conventions.

The purpose of my piece is

_____

The most critical point I make is

_____

What I hope readers will take away from my piece is

_____

Week **1** ## Sentence Fluency
Varying Sentence Types

Week **2** ## Ideas
Developing the Topic

Week **3** ## Organization
Structuring the Body

Focus Mode: Expository

Whether your topic is penguins, Paris, or pole vaulting, the main purpose of expository writing is to inform or explain. That said, your piece does not need to be a list of facts. Actually, it shouldn't be. Think about including fascinating details, intriguing insights, and life experiences. Good expository writing is written in a strong, confident voice—a voice that tells the reader you know what you're talking about.

- Crafting Well-Built Sentences
- **Varying Sentence Types** ·······················
- Capturing Smooth and Rhythmic Flow
- Breaking the "Rules" to Create Fluency

Focus Mode: Expository

Sentence Fluency

❝To create sentence fluency, you have to read with your ears *and* eyes. Make your writing sound as good as it looks by building sentences that flow smoothly from one to the next.❞

Varying Sentence Types

Do you want to know the secret to making your writing sound fresh? Include sentences of all kinds—short ones, long ones, and medium-size ones. Include statements, questions, commands, and exclamations. Mix it up! Varying sentence types gives your writing color and flavor!

How are the sentences in a good piece of writing like fresh produce at the market?

Sentence Types

Sentences serve different purposes.

Simple Statement	declarative	Whales are mammals that live in the ocean.
Question	interrogative	Did you see that whale?
Command	imperative	Look at that whale.
Exclamation	exclamatory	Wow! That whale is huge!

Sentences have different structures.

Simple	a sentence made up of one independent clause that may contain a direct object or prepositional phrase	The blue whale is the largest mammal on earth.
Compound	a sentence made up of two or more independent clauses that are joined by a conjunction such as *and*, *but*, or *or*	Blue whales can be as long as 100 feet, and they can weigh as much as 150 tons.
Complex	a sentence made up of an independent clause and at least one dependent clause	Although blue whales have few predators, they are still classified as endangered, because of widespread hunting of them in the last century.

Warm-Up 10

Sentence Fluency

How is the sentence variety in this paragraph?

Ice pops are good on hot days. It is easy to make ice pops. You pour juice into empty cups. You cover each cup with foil. You poke a stick in the foil. You put your cup in the freezer. That was easy.

Revise the paragraph here or on a separate sheet.

Think About

• Did I include different kinds of sentences?

• Are some of my sentences complex?

• Are some of my sentences simple?

• Did I intermingle sentence types?

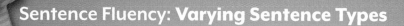

Preview

Nick Veasey, author of *X-treme X-ray*

With a partner, read the information about Nick Veasey and answer the questions below.

1. Nick Veasey believes that many people are "obsessed with image"—that is, too concerned with what is on the surface, such as what their clothes look like. He wants his X-ray photographs to challenge that concern. What do you think he means?

_____

_____

_____

_____

2. After he X-rays people and objects, Veasey processes the film, then cleans and retouches the images to make them crystal clear. How is this similar to the process writers use?

_____

_____

_____

_____

3. Veasey says that beauty is more than skin deep. How might X-rays prove this statement?

_____

_____

_____

_____

Write-On Sheet

[My Spelling Words]

List your nine spelling words for the week here.

1.

2.

3.

4.

5.

6.

7.

8.

9.

> **"** A clear sentence is no accident. Very few sentences come out right the first time, or even the third time. Remember this in moments of despair. **"**
>
> —William Zinsser

[X-Ray Analysis]

Go beneath the surface of *X-treme X-ray* by exploring
the sentences that form its skeleton. Write an example
of each kind of sentence below.

**X-rays?
How x-citing!**

Statement	
Question	
Command	
Exclamation	

Now write a four-sentence summary of *X-treme X-ray*,
using each kind of sentence.

- Finding a Topic
- Focusing the Topic
- **Developing the Topic** ································
- Using Details

Focus Mode: Expository

Ideas

66 **Write about things you care about, wonder about, and notice. Then use lots of juicy, sensory details to describe those things. Great ideas make all the difference in writing!** 99

Developing the Topic

When you develop your topic, you flesh out your main idea. You think deeply about why you're writing the piece and what your reader needs to know to understand it. You stretch to express yourself. Develop your topic to give your writing a chance to fly.

How is a developing writing topic like a developing butterfly?

Techniques for Building Strong Paragraphs

Once you have a focused topic, you need to develop it with facts, examples, and perspectives to build a strong piece of writing. These elements are the building blocks of your paragraph.

1. Add facts

Cheetahs can reach speeds of up to 70 miles per hour.

2. Give an example

In short bursts, the cheetah can run as fast as a car traveling on the highway.

3. Share a personal or expert perspective

If you've never seen a cheetah run before, I can tell you their effortless speed is like poetry in motion.

See how these details work together to create an informative paragraph:

Cheetahs are the fastest land animals.

Cheetahs can reach speeds of up to 70 miles per hour.

In short bursts, the cheetah can run as fast as a car traveling on the highway.

If you've never seen a cheetah run before, I can tell you their effortless speed is like poetry in motion.

Warm-Up 11

Is this paragraph's topic developed?

> Fifth grade is hard. I think it's harder than fourth grade. You do get to do some fun stuff.

Revise the paragraph here or on a separate sheet.

Uh...hello? Can I get some dynamic fifth-grade details here?

Ideas

Think About

- Am I sure my information is right?
- Are my details chock-full of interesting information?
- Have I used details that show new thinking about this idea?
- Will my reader believe what I say about this topic?

Ideas: **Developing the Topic**

Melvin and Gilda Berger, authors of

101 Animal Secrets

Answer the questions below. Discuss your answers with a partner.

1. Melvin Berger studied engineering and music in college and also has a degree in music education. His first book for children was *Science and Music.* Why do you think he chose to write that particular book?

_____

_____

2. According to the Bergers, doing research for one book often leads to ideas for other books. Has something like this ever happened to you? Explain.

_____

_____

3. Other books the Bergers have written include *101 Freaky Animals, Do Tornadoes Really Twist?, Are Mountains Growing Taller?,* and *Flies Taste with Their Feet.* Which of these would you be most interested in reading? Why?

_____

_____

_____

4. Melvin Berger and Gilda Berger usually write books together. How do you think working with another writer could help make you a better writer?

_____

_____

Write-On Sheet

[Focus on Grammar and Usage]

Write two sentences that show correct use of comparative and superlative adverbs.

1. _____

_____

_____

2. _____

_____

_____

> 66 Writing is an exploration. You start from nothing and learn as you go. 99
>
> —E. L. Doctorow

[Animal Secrets Chart]

Choose two animals the Bergers describe in *101 Animal Secrets*. In each organizer below, write the animal name in the top box and three facts, examples, and/or perspectives about each one in the lower boxes.

Psst, I have a secret. I like yams more than bananas.

- Creating the Lead
- Using Sequence Words and Transition Words
- **Structuring the Body** ·····················
- Ending With a Sense of Resolution

Focus Mode: Expository

Organization

Organization

❝Organization is about the structure of a piece of writing. Nothing holds your piece together—or holds a reader's attention—better than sturdy, easy-to-follow organization.❞

Structuring the Body

When you apply this key quality well, you create a piece that is a breeze to read. You present details logically and use them to support your big idea. You slow down and speed up at just the right points. Everything fits together just right. Your piece is strong, complete, and well supported.

How is a well-structured piece of writing like a well-constructed human pyramid?

Traits

Nonfiction Text Structures

The body of a piece of nonfiction can be organized lots of different ways. Here are five structures writers often use:

1. Description or List: a set or group of items

1. Make a snack.
2. Study for social studies test.
3. Soccer practice!
4. Finish science questions.

2. Sequence or Time Order: a series of events or steps in a process

First, sort clothes into darks, whites, and colors. **Then,** load your whites into the washing machine. **Next,** add detergent and bleach, if you are using it.

3. Compare and Contrast: similarities and differences between two people, places, or things

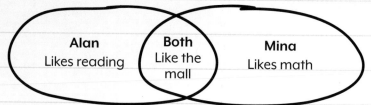

Alan
Likes reading

Both
Like the mall

Mina
Likes math

4. Cause and Effect: an action or idea and how it came to be

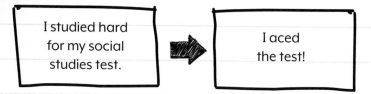

I studied hard for my social studies test. ➡ I aced the test!

5. Problem and Solution: a dilemma of some sort and possible ways out of it

I want to go to the mall, but Mom can't take me.

Ask Alan if his mom can drive.

Take bus with Alan.

Walk to pool instead.

Warm-Up 12

How is this paragraph's structure?

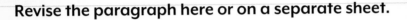

> Recycle this paragraph into something readable...please!

Organization

We put the cans in the red bin. Recycling helps the environment. Our science teacher takes the bins to the recycle center once a week. Separate the glass from the cans. New products can be made from recycled material. We put glass in the green bin. We recycle paper, too.

Revise the paragraph here or on a separate sheet.

Think About

- Have I shown the reader where to slow down and where to speed up?

- Do all the details fit where they are placed?

- Will the reader find it easy to follow my ideas?

- Does the organization help the main idea stand out?

Preview

A Health and Safety Writer

In the spaces below, fill in your thoughts about what a health and safety writer does.

1. What I think the job of health and safety writer might involve:

_____

_____

_____

_____

_____

2. Where I have seen—or might see—writing by a health and safety writer:

_____

_____

_____

_____

_____

3. Questions I have about the job:

_____

_____

_____

_____

_____

Write-On Sheet

[My Spelling Words]

List your nine spelling words for the week here.

1.

2.

3.

4.

5.

6.

7.

8.

9.

> **❝** If you have built castles in the air, your work need not be lost; that is where they should be. Now put the foundations under them. **❞**
>
> —Henry David Thoreau

[Exit the Theater NOW!]

You're watching a movie and—bing!—the screen goes dark. The emergency lights switch on. Create an exit plan in words and pictures to help customers get out of the theater safely.

This reminds me of my favorite movie, *A Bark in the Dark.*

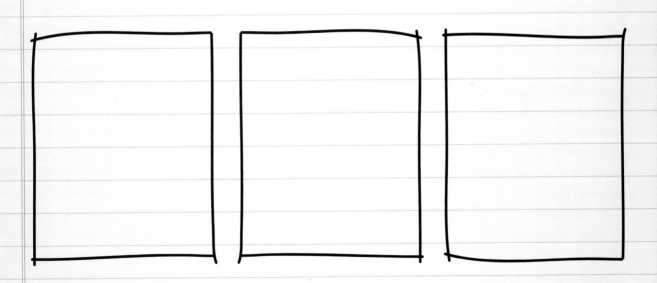

[Expository Publishing Checklist]

Think you are ready to go public with your expository unit project? Use this form to make sure you've covered all the writing bases.

Check. Check.
Quack. Quack.
Check. Check.

I remembered to

☐ include facts that came from reliable sources.

☐ weave in details that show how much I know about my topic.

☐ develop the topic logically from beginning to end.

☐ use a voice that expresses my fascination for the topic.

☐ explain any unusual words, phrases, or concepts.

☐ read my piece aloud to check how it will sound to the reader.

☐ proofread my piece carefully and clean up problems with conventions.

The purpose of my piece is

_____

_____

The part that works the best is

_____

_____

What I hope readers will take away from my piece is

_____

_____

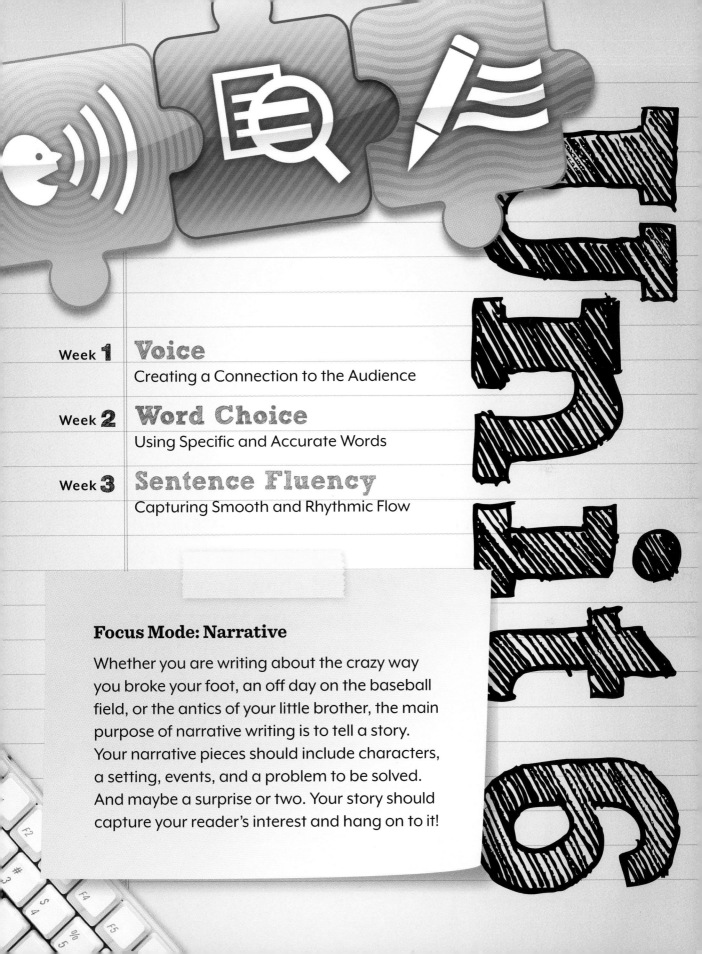

Week 1 **Voice**
Creating a Connection to the Audience

Week 2 **Word Choice**
Using Specific and Accurate Words

Week 3 **Sentence Fluency**
Capturing Smooth and Rhythmic Flow

Focus Mode: Narrative

Whether you are writing about the crazy way you broke your foot, an off day on the baseball field, or the antics of your little brother, the main purpose of narrative writing is to tell a story. Your narrative pieces should include characters, a setting, events, and a problem to be solved. And maybe a surprise or two. Your story should capture your reader's interest and hang on to it!

- Establishing a Tone
- Conveying the Purpose
- Creating a Connection to the Audience ·····································
- Taking Risks to Create Voice

Focus Mode: Narrative

Voice

Voice

66 **Voice is how you speak to readers. It's how you connect to them and show how much you care about your main idea, whether you're writing fiction or nonfiction. It's the energy in your writing.** 99

Creating a Connection to the Audience

If you're having trouble choosing the right tone of voice, think about who is going to read the piece when it's finished. Who is your audience? Use tone to connect with readers so they want to listen to what you have to say. Tell them what you think and feel. Make them understand what matters to you!

Why is it important to connect to your audience, whether you're juggling or writing?

Voice and Audience Match-Up

Read the audiences and the tones of voice below.

- **Audiences**
  friends or family members, your teacher or principal, editor of a newspaper

- **Tones of Voice**
  entertaining, respectful, clever, serious, friendly, scholarly, caring, frustrated, gracious, authoritative, thoughtful, concerned

Now read each passage below. In the boxes, write who you think the audience is and the tone of voice you hear.

The Cave Trail over in Ashland is a treasure. Most of it is easy going but you do have to crawl through a tunnel. The guides are great and the big cave way inside is beautiful.

Audience: _____

Tone: _____

The Cave Trail is SO awesome! It was easy at first—just wet. My shoes got soaked. Then we had to crawl on our bellies. Very, very scary. But it took us to this amazing room with a natural skylight and plants.

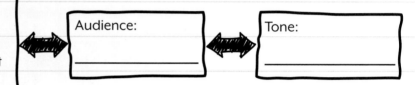

Audience: _____

Tone: _____

The cave tour was wonderful. You really helped me through that long tight tunnel. And you were right: The big room was worth it. I'm glad I did keep going. Thank you.

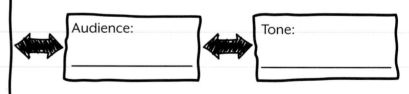

Audience: _____

Tone: _____

Warm-Up 13

I always carry a back*quack.*

How well does this paragraph connect to the audience?

Blue backpacks are good. I like backpacks with lots of pockets and zippers so I can carry lots of things. Sometimes I get bored and like to have something with me to do. It's important to get the right backpack. After all, you carry it every day.

Revise the paragraph here or on a separate sheet.

Think About

• Have I thought about the reader?

• Is this the right voice for my audience?

• Have I shown what matters most to me in this piece?

• Will the reader know how I think and feel about the topic?

Preview

A Copywriter

In the spaces below, answer the questions about the job of a copywriter.

1. You know what a writer does. But what does a copywriter do? What does the "copy" part of this job refer to?

_____

_____

_____

_____

2. Copywriters perform many different writing tasks. They write ads, create packaging, and work on marketing campaigns. Have you seen good marketing campaigns that may have been produced by a copywriter? List a few that stand out for you:

_____

_____

_____

_____

_____

3. What do you think would be the hardest part of being a copywriter?

_____

_____

_____

_____

_____

Write-On Sheet

[Focus on Grammar and Usage]

Write two sentences that contain correct use of irregular verbs.

1. _____

_____

_____

_____

2. _____

_____

_____

_____

> 66 Readers, after all, are making the world with you. You give them the materials, but it's the readers who build that world in their own minds. 99
>
> —**Ursula K. Le Guin**

[A Cool Catalog]

Use your voice. Sell it, baby, sell it!

Pick one of the catalogs you looked at and fill in the following information.

1. Name of catalog: _____

2. Audience for catalog: _____

3. Voice in product descriptions: _____

4. Other things I noticed: _____

_____

_____

Try your hand at writing catalog copy. Choose an item and write the first two sentences of a narrative description of it. Share with a partner what you wrote. What's the verdict? Is it a sale?

_____

_____

_____

_____

_____

_____

_____

_____

_____

_____

Now write the final version on a separate sheet of paper. Add a picture from the catalog.

- Applying Strong Verbs
- Selecting Striking Words and Phrases
- **Using Specific and Accurate Words** ·····························
- Choosing Words That Deepen Meaning

Focus Mode: Narrative

Word Choice

Word Choice

> **Using the right words allows you to show what is happening in your piece or what matters to you about your topic. Precise and accurate words help make your main idea stand out.**

Using Specific and Accurate Words

Specific and accurate words give readers the information they need to understand your writing. For example, saying "The reporter talked about the response to the accident" doesn't grip a reader like this does: "The correspondent reported that hundreds of sea creatures were rescued after the oil spill." Using words like these helps your reader see what you're trying to say.

Why is it important for both a writer and a news reporter to use specific and accurate words?

Word Choice: **Using Specific and Accurate Words**

Pick Precisely!

What are some better words for everyday vehicles? How about for the word *nice*? Fill in each web.

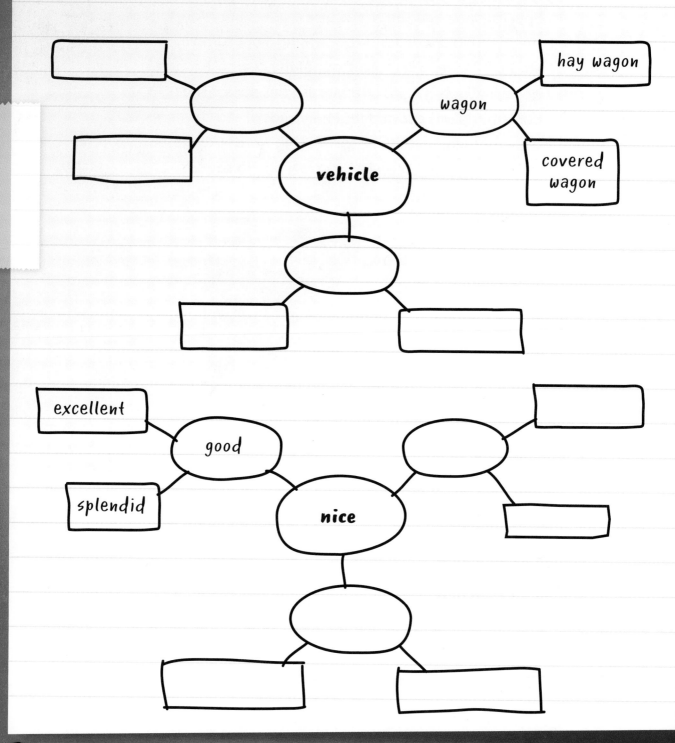

Warm-Up 14

Best friends? Yes. Best words? No!

Does this paragraph contain specific and accurate words?

Want to know about my best friend? My best friend is nice. She let me be the president of our club. She has good ideas for the website. She thought of a symbol to use. We are together a lot. When we're not we still talk. She's funny. We want to be best friends forever.

Revise the paragraph here or on a separate sheet.

Think About

- Have I used nouns and modifiers that help the reader see a picture?

- Did I avoid using words that might confuse the reader?

- Did I try a new word and, if so, check to make sure I used it correctly?

- Are these the best words that can be used?

Word Choice: **Using Specific and Accurate Words**

Pam Muñoz Ryan, author of

Becoming Naomi León

Answer two of the questions below. Discuss your answers with a partner.

1. Pam Muñoz Ryan revises her drafts many times because she believes it improves her writing. How much revising do you typically do? How does it improve your writing?

_____

_____

_____

2. Ryan has a lot of ideas for books, which she keeps in a file so they don't get lost. How do you hang on to ideas for writing?

_____

_____

_____

3. In *Becoming Naomi León,* Ryan uses specific words like *polyester* and *frog voice* to describe the setting and characters. Why do you think she does this?

_____

_____

_____

4. Ryan has written more than twenty other books, including one that features wild horses (*Paint the Wind*), a female stagecoach driver in the old West (*Riding Freedom*), and a young migrant woman living and working on a farm in California (*Esperanza Rising*). Which of these do you think you would you like to read? Why?

_____

_____

_____

Write-On Sheet

[My Spelling Words]

List your nine spelling words for the week here.

1.

2.

3.

4.

5.

6.

7.

8.

9.

> ❝ The one truly reliable shortcut in writing is to choose words that are strong and surefooted to carry the reader on his way. ❞
>
> —William Strunk and E. B. White

[Reverse-Revise It]

Reverse-revise Pam Muñoz Ryan's writing. Rewrite each passage from *Becoming Naomi León,* using bland and nonspecific words.

One of his legs was shorter than the other so he walked like a rocking horse, but other than that, he was just fine.

_____

_____

_____

Gram, in her usual polyester pantsuit and running shoes, was doing her weekly hair set, rolling what little blue hair she had on those new bristle curlers that require no hairpins.

_____

_____

_____

I thought positive every day for a month for more kids at Avocado Acres but all that moved in was a family with a teenager and a brand-new baby.

_____

_____

_____

Before I could write down Gram's suggestion, Owen sneezed, and it was a big one, the kind that sprinkles spittle and left his eyes all teary.

_____

_____

_____

- Crafting Well-Built Sentences
- Varying Sentence Types
- **Capturing Smooth and Rhythmic Flow** ....
- Breaking the "Rules" to Create Fluency

Focus Mode: Narrative

Sentence Fluency

❝To create sentence fluency, you have to read with your ears *and* eyes. Make your writing sound as good as it looks by building sentences that flow smoothly from one to the next.❞

Capturing Smooth and Rhythmic Flow

When you capture smooth and rhythmic flow, you turn tired old sentences into fresh, natural-sounding ones. By varying sentence lengths, starting sentences in different ways, picking just-right words, and using transitions, your writing sounds sweet and moves gracefully.

How are ballroom dancers and good writers alike?

Draw What You Hear

Read the paragraphs below. Which ones flow? Which don't? Draw long, flowing lines or short, choppy lines to show what you hear.

1. The water. Oh the water! A sleek seal, you skim and glide and slide through the glistening water.	**2.** My baby sister sleeps. She cries. She needs her diapers changed. I am tired of my baby sister. Yet I want to see my baby sister.
3. Chores are boring. I hate taking out the trash. I hate cleaning. And doing the dishes.	**4.** We'll scrub and we'll sweep and we'll dust, oh my! We'll polish and scour and shine.
5. My cat moves gracefully. Her tail held high, she prances and purrs as she nudges aside my book to climb onto my lap.	**6.** You are dancing. Don't look at your feet. Or your partner's feet. Don't count steps. Have fun. Or you should stop dancing.

Rewrite one of the choppy paragraphs. Make it smooooooth.

_____

_____

_____

Warm-Up 15

For my family vacation, I'm going rafting on the Rabbit Rapids!

How well does this paragraph flow?

My family will take a vacation. It is for the first week in August. We will swim in a lake. We will camp and hike in the mountains. By Sunday night we will have arrived home. We will be tired and happy. It will have been the best vacation ever.

Revise the paragraph here, or on a separate sheet.

Think About

- Is it easy to read the entire piece aloud?
- Do my sentences flow from one to the next?
- Do individual passages sound smooth when I read them aloud?
- Did I thoughtfully place different sentence types to enhance the main idea?

Preview

Edwidge Danticat, author of

Eight Days: A Story of Haiti

Answer the questions below. Discuss your answers with a partner.

1. As a young girl, Edwidge Danticat listened to stories told by her grandmothers, aunts, and neighbors—stories that influence her writing today. How do other people's stories influence your writing?

_____

_____

_____

2. *Eight Days: A Story of Haiti* is fiction, but it's based on the real stories of survivors of a massive earthquake in Haiti. In what ways can writers use real events to tell stories?

_____

_____

_____

3. Danticat's writing has a smooth and rhythmic flow. How do you think listening to it will help you bring sentence fluency to your writing?

_____

_____

_____

4. When Danticat read *Eight Days* to children living in Haiti who were there during the earthquake, they wanted to talk about their experience. How do you think reading stories about real events might help people make sense of those events?

_____

_____

_____

Write-On Sheet

[Focus on Grammar and Usage]

Write two sentences that contain correct use of the future and future perfect tenses.

1. _____

   _____

   _____

   _____

2. _____

   _____

   _____

   _____

> 66 Edit out loud. Listen to the music of the draft, and tune it so that each paragraph, each line, each word, each space between words creates a beat and melody that supports and advances the meaning of the draft. 99
>
> —**Donald Murray**

[Match It]

Edwidge Danticat's writing is smooth and rhythmic. Read passages from the book below. After each one, write the name of the technique she used.

> ## Techniques to Capture Smooth and Rhythmic Flow
>
> - combine sentences
> - vary sentence lengths, types, and beginnings
> - use sequence and transition words
> - use figurative language like similes, metaphors, and alliteration

These sentences are like freshly shampooed rabbit fur— smooth!

1. And sometimes I cried, because I missed Manman and Papa and my little sister, Justine.

_____

2. I flew my kite. And my best friend, Oscar, who was with me when my house fell, flew his kite, too.

_____

3. Oscar and I played hide-and-seek. We hid in a dark, dusty corner of the house. And not only did Manman and Justine come looking for us, but Papa did, too.

_____

4. And I did get my solo, and it was the best solo ever sung in the church, in the entire country, in the entire world!

_____

[Narrative Publishing Checklist]

Think you are ready to go public with your narrative unit project? Use this form to make sure you've covered all the writing bases.

I was supposed to help out here, but my voice is a little "horse."

I remembered to

☐ develop a fascinating story line with interesting characters.

☐ include a time and a place that work well with the plotline.

☐ tell the story chronologically.

☐ use an active voice to entertain, surprise, and challenge the reader.

☐ choose words that enhance the characters, time, and place.

☐ read my piece aloud to check how it will sound to the reader.

☐ proofread my piece carefully and clean up problems with conventions.

Conventions

The purpose of my piece is

_____

My favorite part is

_____

What I hope readers will find most memorable about my piece is

_____

_____

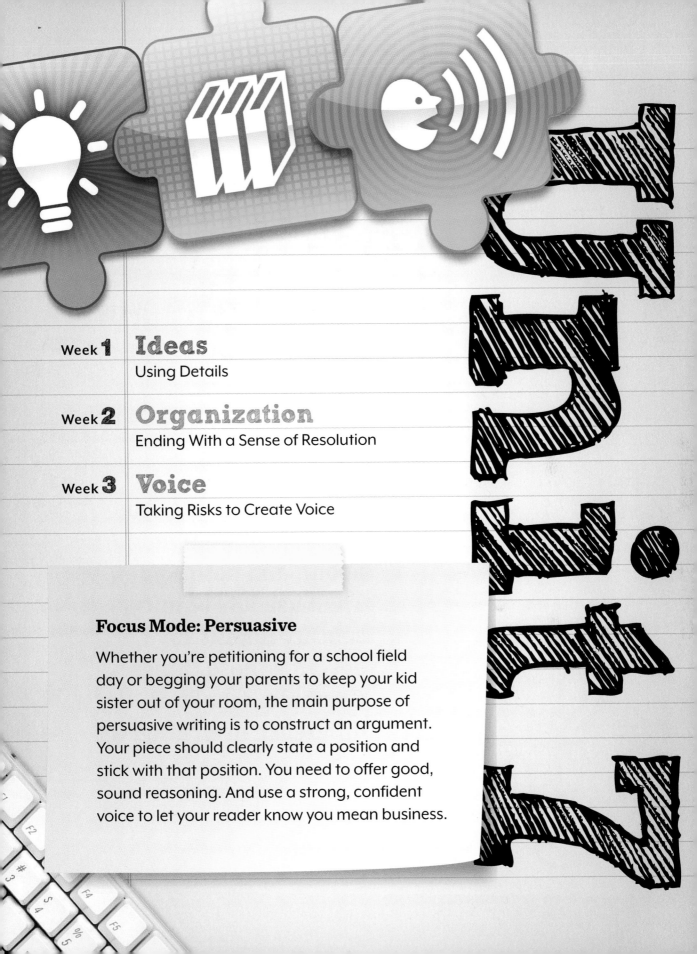

Week **1** ## Ideas
Using Details

Week **2** ## Organization
Ending With a Sense of Resolution

Week **3** ## Voice
Taking Risks to Create Voice

Focus Mode: Persuasive

Whether you're petitioning for a school field day or begging your parents to keep your kid sister out of your room, the main purpose of persuasive writing is to construct an argument. Your piece should clearly state a position and stick with that position. You need to offer good, sound reasoning. And use a strong, confident voice to let your reader know you mean business.

- Finding a Topic
- Focusing the Topic
- Developing the Topic
- **Using Details** ·····································

Ideas

66 **Write about things you care about, wonder about, and notice. Then use lots of juicy, sensory details to describe those things. Great ideas make all the difference in writing!** 99

Using Details

When you write, you want your readers to see exactly what you are thinking. To help them, use details. Details help readers imagine how something looks, feels, smells, sounds, or tastes. They make your ideas clearer and easier to understand. Your piece goes from dull to dazzling!

How is choosing beads for a necklace like adding details to a piece of writing?

The Senses Show It

Using words and phrases that appeal to the senses is one way to add details to your writing. Fill in the chart with more examples of sensory words and phrases.

Sight	Hearing	Smell	Taste	Touch
glistening	crackling	pungent	salty	smooth

Sentences That *Tell* and Sentences That *Show*

Identify which sentences simply *tell* you something about the subject, and which ones *show* it to you instead. Write "tell" or "show" in the blanks beside each example.

_____ Thunder rumbles daily and gray daggers of rain are common.

_____ The weather is bad.

_____ It's important to brush long-haired cats often.

_____ Daily brushing makes your long-haired cat satiny smooth.

_____ This lemonade tastes good.

_____ Luscious Lemon Coolers bubble down your throat in a refreshing stream.

Warm-Up 16

How are the details in this paragraph?

The cafeteria should serve better food. They serve lots of stuff that isn't good for you. They should serve food that's good for you. Maybe kids would eat it.

Revise the paragraph here or on a separate sheet.

I like Banana Pizza Day. Very a-peel-ing!

Think About

- Did I create a picture in the reader's mind?
- Did I use details that draw upon the five senses (sight, hearing, smell, taste, touch)?
- Do my details stay on the main topic?
- Did I stretch for details beyond the obvious?

Ideas: **Using Details**

A Publicity Writer

In the spaces below, fill in your thoughts about the job of a publicity writer.

1. What I think is involved in the job of a publicity writer:

_____

_____

_____

_____

2. Different places I might see work by a publicity writer:

_____

_____

_____

_____

_____

3. What are some of the questions readers have about an important person that a publicity writer might include in an article:

_____

_____

_____

_____

_____

Write-On Sheet

Ideas: Using Details

[My Spelling Words]

List your nine spelling words for the week here.

1.

2.

3.

4.

5.

6.

7.

8.

9.

> 66 The greatest writers . . . are effective largely because they deal in particulars and report the details that matter. Their words call up pictures. 99
>
> —William Strunk and E. B. White

[A Must-See]

Pick one of these "must-see" destinations.

- tropical beach

- theme park

- mountain resort

- wilderness area

Give your destination a name, such as Balmy Breeze Beach.

Hmmm... Have you been to Magic Monkey Mountain? It's fantastic!

Name: _____

Fill in the chart with details about what visitors will . . .

see	hear	smell	taste	feel

Write a description of your destination. Read it aloud to a partner to make sure he or she can picture exactly what you are describing. If you need to, replace words that *tell* with details that *show*.

_____

_____

_____

_____

Create your brochure on a separate sheet of paper. Use details that make your readers feel as if they are already on vacation.

- Creating the Lead
- Using Sequence Words and Transition Words
- Structuring the Body
- **Ending With a Sense of Resolution** ·····················

Focus Mode: Persuasive

Organization

❝**Organization is about the structure of a piece of writing. Nothing holds your piece together—or holds a reader's attention—better than sturdy, easy-to-follow organization.**❞

Ending With a Sense of Resolution

The conclusion is the final touch on a piece of writing—its last lines. A good conclusion ties up all the loose ends and makes your piece feel complete and resolved. It's your last word, so be sure to write something that will satisfy your readers.

What's the similarity between the end of a special meal and the ending of a great piece of writing?

Cooking Up a Conclusion

Here are four techniques—or "ingredients"—writers use to cook up an ending that's satisfying to readers.

Question to the Reader: What would happen if everyone gave just one hour of their time to make our community a better place?

Call to Action: Turn off your television for one hour a week and go volunteer for a cause you care about. You'll be improving yourself and your community.

Quote: Booker T. Washington once said, "If you want to lift yourself up, lift up someone else."

Final Example: I first started reading to Mrs. Johnson because I *had to.* Now I read to her each week because I *want to.*

Now let's see how our conclusion turns out when we mix together two of these ingredients.

1 final example
1 quote
Mix well for a tasty conclusion.

I first started reading to Mrs. Johnson because I *had* to. Now I read to her each week because I *want* to. As Booker T. Washington once said, "If you want to lift yourself up, lift up someone else."

Now you try it. Take two ingredients and cook up your own tasty conclusion on a separate sheet of paper.

Warm-Up 17

The movie did have a good ending. Too bad this paragraph doesn't!

How is this paragraph's conclusion?

Maybe you don't believe me. I thought the noises I heard were from a monster. They weren't. I guess I was feeling scared from watching a scary movie before bed. Don't watch scary movies at night.

Revise the paragraph here or on a separate sheet.

Organization

Think About

- Have I wrapped up all the loose ends?

- Have I ended at the best place?

- Do I have an ending that makes my writing feel finished?

- Did I leave the reader with something to think about?

Preview

Molly Bang, author of *Common Ground*

Answer the questions below. Discuss your answers with a partner.

1. Many of Molly Bang's books, including *Common Ground*, are about science. Her husband is a scientist and her parents were both scientists. Although she grew up surrounded with science, Bang is not a scientist. Do you think you need to be a scientist to write well about science? Explain.

_____

_____

_____

_____

2. Bang believes it is important to show emotions in her illustrations—and not only as expressions on people's faces. How do you think she might do that? How do you show emotion in your own writing?

_____

_____

_____

_____

3. Molly Bang begins *Common Ground* with these words: "May we make our decisions for the seventh generation." What do you think that means?

_____

_____

_____

_____

_____

Write-On Sheet

[Focus on Grammar and Usage]

Write two sentences that contain a dependent clause and an independent clause.

1. _____

   _____

   _____

2. _____

   _____

   _____

66 Envisioning the end is enough to put the means into motion. **99**

—Dorothea Brande

[Finding Common Ground]

The villagers in *Common Ground* and people today are similar in some ways—and different in others. As you listen to the book, complete the Venn diagram to compare and contrast the villagers and people today.

Is this a game?! How do I play?

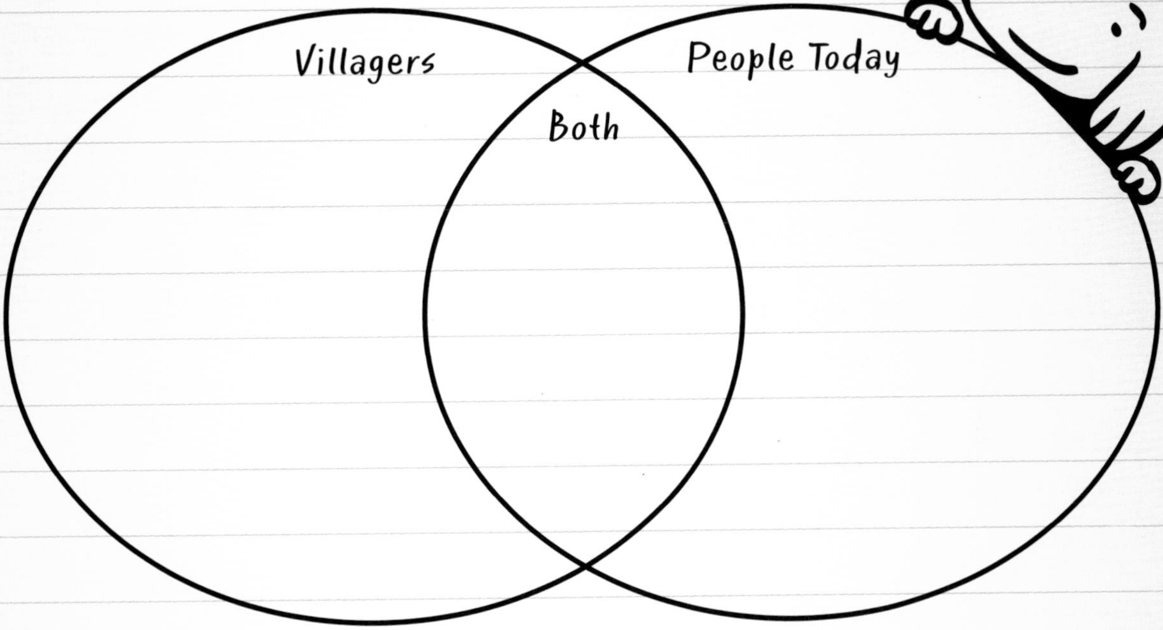

Villagers   People Today

Both

How does Molly Bang's ending connect the villagers to people today? What is she trying to persuade her readers to believe?

_____

_____

_____

_____

_____

_____

_____

- Establishing a Tone
- Conveying the Purpose
- Creating a Connection to the Audience
- **Taking Risks to Create Voice** ······················

Focus Mode: Persuasive

Voice

Voice

" Voice is how you speak to readers. It's how you connect to them and show how much you care about your main idea, whether you're writing fiction or nonfiction. It's the energy in your writing. "

Taking Risks to Create Voice

The best writers take risks. They might take on new topics, play with voice, or experiment with words. If you want your writing to reach new heights, you can't be afraid to take chances and try new things. Surprise your readers. In the process, you might surprise yourself!

What do a snowboarder and a writer who takes risks have in common?

Walk in These Shoes

Writers who take risks write from different points of view—adults, children, animals, even objects. In other words, they're not afraid to walk in the shoes of all different kinds of characters.

To write from a different point of view, ask yourself these questions:

- What is this character thinking?

- What would the character say and how would he or she say it?

- How does the character sound: bashful? boisterous? babyish? gruff?

- How does the character feel?

- Think *why*. Why does the character think, act, sound, and feel that way?

Choose a pair of shoes and describe below the person who might wear them. Then, on a separate sheet, write from that person's point of view by explaining where you're going in those shoes and what you're going to do.

_____

_____

_____

_____

Warm-Up 18

Did the writer of this paragraph take any risks?

> You should get a library card. They are free. You can get books and movies. You can get books sent to your house.

Revise the paragraph here or on a separate sheet.

This writer needs to borrow a voice! Maybe you can lend yours...

Think About

• Have I used words that are not ordinary?

• Is my writing interesting, fresh, and original?

• Have I tried to make my writing sound like me?

• Have I tried something different from what I've done before?

Preview

Mark Teague, author of *LaRue for Mayor*

With a partner, answer three of the questions below.

1. Mark Teague's books start as "notebooks full of sketches and scribbles, strange little drawings, and phrases." Do you keep a notebook? If not, how does your writing start?

   _____

   _____

   _____

2. Teague says his books usually spring from something in his real life but don't actually look like his life. Do you think it's important to start with something you know? Explain.

   _____

   _____

   _____

3. Teague's books often address common fears, such as imagining monsters in closets and being late for school. How do you think writing about a specific fear helps the writer (and readers) deal with that fear?

   _____

   _____

   _____

4. The main character in *LaRue for Mayor* is a dog. Teague says that he writes books with dog characters because they are like comical people. Knowing this, what are your predictions about the book's tone and voice?

   _____

   _____

   _____

Write-On Sheet

[My Spelling Words]

List your nine spelling words for the week here.

1.

2.

3.

4.

5.

6.

7.

8.

9.

> 66 If you don't allow yourself the possibility of writing something very, very bad, it would be hard to write something very good. 99
>
> —Steven Galloway

[Upsetting the Hot Dog Cart]

The best writers aren't afraid to upset the apple cart—or in Mark Teague's case, the hot dog cart. On the hot dogs below, write unusual, original things his character, Ike LaRue, says.

Hot dogs filled with spicy sentences. Now that's a meal I could quack about!

Now, on a separate sheet, write a short letter from Ike to Mrs. LaRue convincing her that the hot dog cart incident during the swearing-in ceremony was nothing to worry about and, in fact, really had "nothing to do with me."

[Persuasive Publishing Checklist]

Think you are ready to go public with your extended persuasive project? Use this form to make sure you've covered all the writing bases.

You've persuaded this Presentation penguin!

I remembered to

☐ state my position on the topic clearly and stick with it while also exposing weaknesses in other positions.

☐ offer good, sound reasoning based on solid facts, opinions, and examples that originate from reliable, objective sources.

☐ develop my argument logically, using solid reasoning from beginning to end.

☐ use a compelling, confident voice to add credibility.

☐ explain any unusual words, phrases, or concepts.

☐ read my piece aloud to check how it will sound to the reader.

☐ proofread my piece carefully and clean up problems with conventions.

The purpose of my piece is

_____

The most critical point I make is

_____

What I hope readers will take away from my piece is

_____

_____

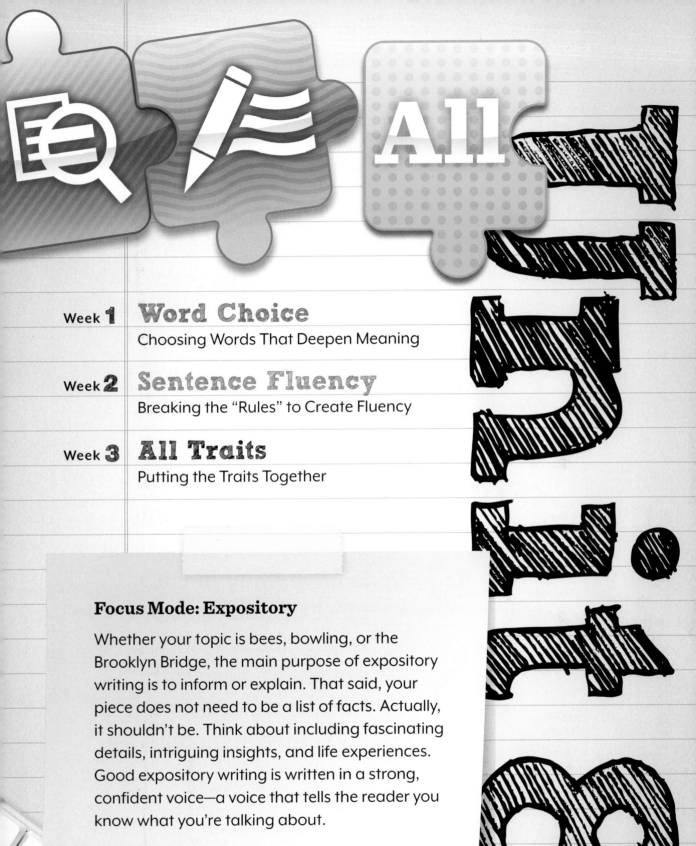

All

Week 1 **Word Choice**
Choosing Words That Deepen Meaning

Week 2 **Sentence Fluency**
Breaking the "Rules" to Create Fluency

Week 3 **All Traits**
Putting the Traits Together

Focus Mode: Expository

Whether your topic is bees, bowling, or the Brooklyn Bridge, the main purpose of expository writing is to inform or explain. That said, your piece does not need to be a list of facts. Actually, it shouldn't be. Think about including fascinating details, intriguing insights, and life experiences. Good expository writing is written in a strong, confident voice—a voice that tells the reader you know what you're talking about.

- Applying Strong Verbs
- Selecting Striking Words and Phrases
- Using Specific and Accurate Words
- **Choosing Words That Deepen Meaning** ....

Focus Mode: Expository

Word Choice

Word Choice

66 Using the right words allows you to show what is happening in your piece or what matters to you about your topic. Precise and accurate words help make your main idea stand out. 99

Choosing Words That Deepen Meaning

Good writers take their time. They stop to think about the best words to use—words that make their message clear. So instead of using the first words that come to mind, dig deeper. Choose words that say exactly what you mean, paint pictures, and bring color to your writing. Give your readers something to think about.

How are words that deepen the meaning like a rainbow shining through falling rain?

Word Choice: Choosing Words That Deepen Meaning

A Figurative Feast

Writers often use figurative language to express an idea more deeply and imaginatively. Here are four types of figurative language. Read the definitions and examples and add your own example to each one.

1. **Simile:** uses *like* or *as* to compare two things.

   Example: *Her eyes were like rivers about to overflow.*

   My example: _____

   _____

   _____

2. **Metaphor:** says one thing *is* something else.

   Example: *That baseball glove in the store window was a flower—and I was a hungry bee.*

   My example: _____

   _____

   _____

3. **Personification:** gives human qualities to something that is not human.

   Example: *The sun smiled down on a river that was giggling its way to town.*

   My example: _____

   _____

   _____

4. **Onomatopoeia:** imitates the sound it represents.

   Example: *Whoosh! The hawk swooped down and with a loud "screee!" snatched the panicked mouse from the ground and into the air.*

   My example: _____

   _____

Warm-Up 19

Pancakes are delicious. But this paragraph sure isn't!

Do the words in this paragraph deepen its meaning?

You can make pancakes any time. You need pancake mix and other things. Stir the ingredients together. Cook the pancakes and put on syrup. They taste good.

Revise the paragraph here or on a separate sheet.

Think About

- Did I think carefully about the words I chose?
- Have I tried to avoid repeating words?
- Will my words capture the reader's imagination?
- Have I found the best way to express myself?

Preview

A Game Company Writer

In the spaces below, fill in your thoughts about what a game company writer does.

1. What I think is involved in the job of game company writer:

_____

_____

_____

_____

_____

2. How I think a game company writer prepares for his or her job:

_____

_____

_____

_____

_____

3. Some of my favorite games and how I learned to play them:

_____

_____

_____

_____

_____

Write-On Sheet

[Focus on Conventions]

Write two sentences—one that correctly uses apostrophes in plural possessives and one that correctly uses contractions.

1. _____

   _____

   _____

2. _____

   _____

   _____

> ❝ Do not say a little in many words, but a great deal in a few. ❞
>
> **—Pythagoras**

[Let's Play]

Choose one of these games or sports.

soccer football	four square basketball	tennis capture the flag

Game or sport I chose: _____

Complete the chart by filling in details about what equipment is needed to play your game or sport and how to play it. Assume your readers have never played the game or sport, so be sure to make your ideas clear.

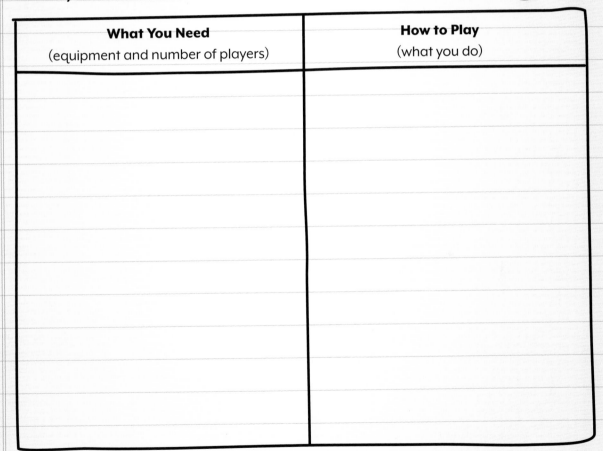

What You Need (equipment and number of players)	How to Play (what you do)

On a separate sheet of paper, write a description of the game or sport you chose. Remember to dig for just the right words and phrases to deepen your meaning—and make readers *want* to play.

- Crafting Well-Built Sentences
- Varying Sentence Types
- Capturing Smooth and Rhythmic Flow
- **Breaking the "Rules" to Create Fluency** ....

Focus Mode: Expository

Sentence Fluency

Sentence Fluency

"To create sentence fluency, you have to read with your ears *and* eyes. Make your writing sound as good as it looks by building sentences that flow smoothly from one to the next."

Breaking the "Rules" to Create Fluency

You have learned many rules for writing sentences correctly. "Always include a subject and verb." "Don't start a sentence with a conjunction." "Never use a word as a sentence." But wait! To bring rhythm to your writing, you might need to break rules sometimes. Interjections can highlight points. And sentence fragments can add style. Shake it up. Break it up. Keep it flowing. Yes!

How is breaking the "rules" of writing like breaking the "rules" of fashion or music?

Rules to Break

Some basic rules of writing:

1. **Don't use overly casual, everyday language.**

2. **Don't use fragments. Every sentence should have a subject and predicate.**

3. **Don't start all your sentences the same way.**

4. **Don't start sentences with a conjunction, such as *but* and *and*.**

Which rules are broken in the examples below? Which example is more successful in conveying its message effectively?

Example 1:

Justin was the reason Jenna had to share her room. Justin was the reason Jenna had to be quiet when she got home from school. Justin was the reason that everything changed. But Mom and Dad didn't understand why Jenna didn't like Justin. Neither did Jenna's friends. They thought Justin was adorable. They loved his tiny little outfits. They loved his perfect fingers and toes. "Can baby brothers be exchanged?" Jenna asked her mother. "Probably not, huh?" she answered for herself.

Rules broken: _____

_____

Example 2:

Jenna thought it wasn't fun to have a new baby brother. Baby brothers cry a lot. Her baby brother was boring. She had to be quiet all the time. Her friends liked her baby brother. But she just wished her parents would take him back. That probably won't happen though.

Rules broken: _____

_____

Warm-Up 20

Did this writer break the rules to create fluency?

Wordsmiths, unite!
Break rules and write!

Book reports are trouble. You need to pick the right book. The right book is important. Book reports are easy if you pick the right book.

Revise the paragraph here or on a separate sheet.

Think About

- Did I use fragments with style and purpose?
- Did I use informal language when it made sense to do so?
- Does my dialogue sound authentic?
- Did I try weaving in exclamations and single words to add emphasis?

Preview

Andrea Davis Pinkney, author of

Duke Ellington

Answer the questions below. Discuss your answers with a partner.

1. Andrea Davis Pinkney's mother was an English teacher. She often brought home books for Andrea to read. How do you think this helped inspire Andrea to become a writer?

_____

_____

_____

_____

_____

2. Ideas for writing "pop into my head at the oddest times"—like while riding the subway, Andrea Davis Pinkney has said. What does that tell you about the kind of person she is?

_____

_____

_____

_____

_____

3. The illustrator of *Duke Ellington* is Brian Pinkney, Andrea Davis Pinkney's husband. Would you like to work with a family member? Why or why not?

_____

_____

_____

_____

_____

Write-On Sheet

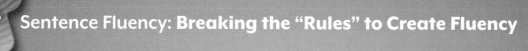

[Focus on Conventions]

Write two sentences—one that is a complete sentence with a subject and predicate and one that has a dependent clause linked to an independent clause.

1. _____

   _____

   _____

2. _____

   _____

   _____

> **"** If you obey all the rules, you miss all the fun. **"**
>
> —Katharine Hepburn

[Sentence Fluency Four Square]

Fill in the squares with an example of how Andrea Davis Pinkney broke each rule. Make a note about how each "break" makes her writing more appealing and fluent.

> The author is Pinkney. I have a pink nose.

Don't use overly casual, everyday language.	Don't use fragments.

Don't start all your sentences the same way.	Don't start sentences with a conjunction.

- Ideas
- Organization
- Voice
- Word Choice
- Sentence Fluency
- Conventions
- Presentation

Focus Mode: Expository

All Traits

"The traits give you the language to talk about writing. You've learned a lot about the traits—what they are, how to look for them in your writing, and how to use them when you prewrite, draft, revise, and edit. What makes the traits so great? They help make YOU a great writer!"

Putting the Traits Together

All year, you've been breaking down your writing and looking at it by trait. Now it's time to look at the five revision traits at the same time—and see how far you've come as a writer.

What do a jigsaw puzzle and a piece of writing have in common?

Trait Strong

Ideas, Organization, Voice, Word Choice, and Sentence Fluency work together to help you create strong writing. Read the short definitions of each trait below and then look for evidence of the traits in the paragraph. Underline what you find and/or make notes in the margin.

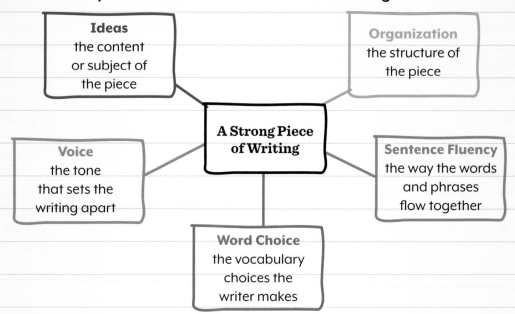

Ideas
the content or subject of the piece

Organization
the structure of the piece

A Strong Piece of Writing

Voice
the tone that sets the writing apart

Sentence Fluency
the way the words and phrases flow together

Word Choice
the vocabulary choices the writer makes

When Mom first asked me to babysit my little brother while she worked in the garden, I groaned. Now that I've done it a few times, I've got some tips and tricks that make babysitting a breeze: 1.) Snacks. Lots of them! A box of raisins or some graham crackers usually stop the tears in their tracks. 2.) Books. A babysitter's best friend. Kids adore stories, and if you're reading together, they're not coloring on the walls or drinking from the dog dish. 3.) Games and songs. Little kids like to sing and dance and play simple games. Make them up. It really doesn't matter. 4.) Emergency numbers. Good to have posted by the phone even though Mom's a holler away. Now when Mom asks me to babysit, I say "sure." I get to spend time with my little bro and score some extra dollars, too!

Warm-Up 21

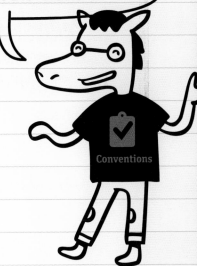

Attention! Calling all traits. Your help is needed on page 213. Now!

How well does this writer use all the traits?

You shouldn't be late for school. Teachers don't like that. They don't like lots of things. It's easy not to be late. There are tips.

Revise the paragraph here or on a separate sheet.

Think About

- Does my writing show that I understand my topic?
- Are my details in the best possible order?
- Can the reader tell I care about this idea?
- Have I painted a picture with words?
- Does my writing sound good when read aloud?

Preview

Gary Paulsen, author of

Puppies, Dogs, and Blue Northers

Answer the questions below. Share your ideas with a partner.

1. Gary Paulsen's life changed when he discovered that books were great companions. How have books affected your life?

_____

_____

_____

2. Gary Paulsen left home when he was fourteen and supported himself by taking on many different jobs. What impact do you think that experience has had on his writing?

_____

_____

_____

3. Dogs, dog sledding, and people's relationships with dogs and nature are common themes in Gary Paulsen's work. Do you think they make his writing style more imaginative or realistic? Explain.

_____

_____

_____

4. Gary Paulsen enjoys writing for and meeting young people. If you met Mr. Paulsen, what would you like to talk with him about?

_____

_____

_____

Write-On Sheet

[Focus on Conventions]

Write two sentences, one that uses an irregular verb correctly and one that uses the future tense correctly.

1. _____

_____

_____

2. _____

_____

_____

> 66 Take out another notebook, pick up another pen, and just write, just write, just write.... Say yes, stay alive, be awake. Just write. 99
>
> —Natalie Goldberg

[The Total Package]

Gary Paulsen uses the five revision traits effectively in *Puppies, Dogs, and Blue Northers.* Complete the chart by giving an example of each trait or explaining how Paulsen applied the trait. With a partner, discuss how Paulsen applied the Conventions and Presentation traits.

Ideas	
Organization	
Word Choice	
Voice	
Sentence Fluency	

[Expository Publishing Checklist]

Think you are ready to go public with your expository unit project? Use this form to make sure you've covered all the writing bases.

Oh yeah, I have some words for you: GREAT JOB!

I remembered to

☐ include facts that came from reliable sources.

☐ weave in details that show how much I know about my topic.

☐ develop the topic logically from beginning to end.

☐ use a voice that expresses my fascination for the topic.

☐ explain any unusual words, phrases, or concepts.

☐ read my piece aloud to check how it will sound to the reader.

☐ proofread my piece carefully and clean up problems with conventions.

The purpose of my piece is

_____

_____

The part that works the best is

_____

_____

What I hope readers will take away from my piece is

_____

_____

Week

1

Reflecting on Myself as a Writer

Week

2

Saying Good-bye to My Writing Folder

Week

3

Celebrating Our Accomplishments

Week

4

Cleaning Up and Having Fun

Wrapping Up the Year

As our writing year together draws to a close, let's look back at what you've learned about the traits and how they've helped you improve your writing. We'll stop and admire what you've written, look ahead to next year, and celebrate your accomplishments—the big ones and the little ones.

It's time to look back at everything you've learned this year about being a good writer. First you'll investigate one of the traits—what's easy about it, what's hard about it, and how it helped you improve your writing. Then you'll look ahead by writing a letter of introduction to next year's writing teacher.

Trait Speech Planner

Make notes about your assigned trait in order to get ready to write a speech with your group.

1. Trait: _____

2. The voice this trait would use when speaking:

   _____

   _____

3. Sample writing, from a mentor text or other text, that demonstrates this trait:

   _____

   _____

   Sample from my own writing:

   _____

   _____

4. What makes this trait great:

   _____

   _____

5. Ideas for posters to hang or slides to project:

   _____

   _____

   _____

[Trait Speech Checklist]

Once your group's speech is drafted, use this checklist to make sure it's your best work possible.

- ☐ Is it clear why this trait is important?
- ☐ Is the organization logical? Do our points build on one another and flow naturally?
- ☐ Did we include examples from mentor texts and from our own writing?
- ☐ Did we read the speech aloud to check for sentence fluency?
- ☐ Did we proofread to make sure our grammar is correct?
- ☐ Do our visual aids support our main points?

[Letter-Writing Checklist]

Use this list to help you decide what to say in your letter to next year's teacher.

- ☐ What kind of writing do I enjoy most?
- ☐ What is my greatest strength as a writer?
- ☐ What part of writing do I find the most challenging?
- ☐ What is a favorite book or magazine of mine from this year?
- ☐ What question would I like to ask next year's teacher?

Thinking Ahead: Writing Goals

Look back at page 11 and read your writing goals for this year. Give an example of something you know about writing that shows you've met one of your goals.

_____

_____

_____

_____

_____

_____

_____

Now think about what you still want to improve and write about it here.

_____

_____

_____

_____

_____

_____

_____

Saying Good-bye to My Writing Folder

Think about all the writing you did this year. Does any piece in particular stand out in your mind? Do you remember the first benchmark paper you created? This week, you will

1 write a paper in the same mode and on the same general topic as your beginning-of-year benchmark piece. Then you'll reread the original and compare the two pieces to see what you've learned.

2 clean out your writing folder and write a reflection from the point of view of the folder.

Plan Your Paper

Use this page to plan your end-of-year benchmark paper. Identify the mode and topic here. Then use the space below to brainstorm around your topic, make notes about key ideas or words to include, or create a graphic organizer such as a web or sequence chart to help organize your ideas.

Mode: _____   **Topic:** _____

Saying Good-bye to My Writing Folder

Mock Reflections

Read these examples to give you an idea of what your reflection might include.

I Remember

<u>I was just a little folder. No marks, no tears, no doodles—just a clean folder, straight out of the box. I was excited. School had just begun and I'd heard today was the day I'd be matched to my writer. Would it be a boy or a girl? Would he or she like me and treat me nicely or just toss me aside with indifference? Oh, look—it's my turn! And the name of my new owner is _____.</u>

Hey! Take It Easy!

<u>Ouch. That's how I feel when you cram me back into the file with the other folders. Take it easy, kid. I'm just made out of paper, you know. If you want me to be around a long time, holding your writing papers and keeping things together, then you need to treat me kindly. Is that asking for too much?</u>

My Life as a Writing Folder

Possible formats for my reflection

blog	poster
collage	quotations
drawing	song
e-mail	speech
essay	story
letter	text message
poem	

My format:

_____

I might include these things in my reflection.

What I enjoy about being a writing folder:

_____

_____

What is not so great about being a writing folder:

_____

_____

My fondest memory of my year with this writer:

_____

_____

Some words of advice to users of writing folders:

_____

_____

_____

Celebrating Our Accomplishments

We celebrate holidays, special events, and now YOU, the writer! Yes, this week you and your classmates will continue wrapping up your writing year. Throw yourself into the fun activities your teacher has planned for you. It's guaranteed to be a week to remember!

Quick Skit Voting Sheet

Rate each skit for ideas, organization, and overall entertainment impact. Use a scale of 1–3 points, with 3 being the highest.

Quick Skit Scorecard

	Ideas	Organization	Entertainment Impact	Total Points
Group 1				
Group 2				
Group 3				
Group 4				
Group 5				

Quick Skit Ballot

Favorite Skit:

Total Score:

Celebrating Our Accomplishments

I'm a Fan

Choose your favorite mentor text from the year. Then fill in the planner to organize your fan mail to its author.

The title of the book I liked the best this year is

_____

Written by _____

Illustrated by _____

I like this author and illustrator because

1. _____

2. _____

3. _____

If I had only one thing to tell the author, I'd want him or her to

know _____

I'd like the illustrator to know _____

_____

Ways to deliver the letter:

The publisher's address or e-mail is _____

_____

The author or illustrator's website is _____

_____

_____

Sundae Mix-Ins

Translate the traits into "yummies" for frozen yogurt treats—or supplies you'll need for a yogurt sundae buffet. Write down your group's trait, words you associate with that trait, and foods and supplies that represent those words.

Our trait:

_____

Key words for the trait:

_____

_____

Key Words	Foods and Supplies That Represent the Words

Cleaning Up and Having Fun

This is it—the final week. You'll clean up your own space and help your teacher clean up the classroom. You'll also play some writing-related games. You may be surprised at how good you are at them after all the hard work you've put in as a writer. You've learned a lot—now it's time to have some fun and say so long!

Word Search

Use a pencil or highlighter to circle the writing traits words in the Word Search puzzle. The words go forward, backward, up, and down.

audience	body	details	fluency	focus
ideas	lead	meaning	organization	patterns
purpose	resolution	rhythm	sequence	specific
tone	topic	verbs	voice	

f	g	t	q	r	n	t	y	u	i	p	x	a	z	e	p
m	g	o	r	g	a	n	i	z	a	t	i	o	n	s	z
y	u	p	t	j	g	j	f	d	u	v	b	m	o	k	l
s	v	i	b	a	f	s	g	h	d	e	t	a	i	l	s
f	o	c	u	s	v	b	h	g	i	j	j	a	t	z	p
l	l	g	k	e	a	r	b	x	e	c	b	l	u	p	e
u	x	v	q	q	s	e	f	b	n	v	k	b	l	n	c
e	a	e	c	u	b	v	c	i	z	h	b	o	n	i
n	u	n	s	e	s	o	d	a	e	l	p	a	s	k	f
c	h	o	n	n	h	f	z	i	x	s	v	j	e	s	i
y	b	t	r	c	l	b	w	l	t	o	a	q	r	f	c
h	j	a	e	e	s	o	p	r	u	p	y	v	q	f	x
n	b	g	t	n	f	d	d	m	r	z	u	o	x	e	v
r	h	y	t	h	m	y	m	m	e	a	n	i	n	g	w
n	m	g	a	j	m	s	f	f	v	p	v	c	k	c	g
z	v	m	p	x	l	j	v	s	h	s	a	e	d	i	s

Ideas

the content of your piece—its central message and the details that support that message

6 EXPERT

HIGH

My topic is well developed and focused. My piece contains specific, interesting, and accurate details, and new thinking about this topic.

- I have a clear central theme or a simple, original story line.
- I've narrowed my theme or story line to create a focused piece that is a pleasure to read.
- I've included original information to support my main idea.
- I've included specific, interesting, and accurate details that will create pictures in the reader's mind.

5 WELL DONE

4 ALMOST THERE

MIDDLE

My piece includes many general observations about the topic, but lacks focus and clear, accurate details. I need to elaborate.

- I've stayed on the topic, but my theme or story line is too broad.
- I haven't dug into the topic in a logical, focused way.
- My unique perspective on this topic is not coming through as clearly as it could.
- The reader may have questions after reading this piece because my details leave some questions unanswered.

3 MAKING STRIDES

2 ON MY WAY

LOW

I'm still thinking about the theme or story line for this piece. So far, I've only explored possibilities.

- I've jotted down some ideas for topics, but it's a hodgepodge.
- Nothing in particular stands out as important in my piece.
- I have not written much. I may have only restated the assignment.
- My details are thin and need to be checked for accuracy.

1 GETTING STARTED

Organization

the internal structure of your piece—the thread of logic, the pattern of meaning

6 EXPERT

HIGH

My details unfold in a logical order. The structure makes reading my piece a breeze.

- My beginning grabs the reader's attention.
- I've used sequence and transition words to guide the reader.
- All of my details fit together logically and move along smoothly.
- My ending gives the reader a sense of closure and something to think about.

5 WELL DONE

4 ALMOST THERE

MIDDLE

My piece's organization is pretty basic and predictable. I have the three essential ingredients, a beginning, middle, and end, but that's about it.

- My beginning is clear, but unoriginal. I've used a technique that writers use all too often.
- I've used simple sequence and transition words that stand out too much.
- Details need to be added or moved around to create a more logical flow of ideas.
- My ending needs work; it's pretty canned.

3 MAKING STRIDES

2 ON MY WAY

LOW

My piece doesn't make much sense because I haven't figured out a way to organize it. The details are jumbled together at this point.

- My beginning doesn't indicate where I'm going or why I'm going there.
- I have not grouped ideas or connected them using sequence and transition words.
- With no sense of order, it will be a challenge for the reader to sort out how the details relate.
- I haven't figured out how to end this piece.

1 GETTING STARTED

Voice

the tone of the piece—your personal stamp, which is achieved through an understanding of purpose and audience

HIGH

6 EXPERT

I've come up with my own "take" on the topic. I had my audience and purpose clearly in mind as I wrote and presented my ideas in an original way.

- My piece is expressive, which shows how much I care about my topic.
- The purpose for this piece is clear, and I've used a tone that suits that purpose.
- There is no doubt in my mind that the reader will understand how I think and feel about my topic.
- I've expressed myself in some new, original ways.

5 WELL DONE

MIDDLE

4 ALMOST THERE

My feelings about the topic come across as uninspired and predictable. The piece is not all that expressive, nor does it reveal a commitment to the topic.

- In a few places, my authentic voice comes through, but only in a few.
- My purpose for writing this piece is unclear to me, so the tone feels "off."
- I've made little effort to connect with the reader; I'm playing it safe.
- This piece sounds like lots of others on this topic. It's not very original.

3 MAKING STRIDES

LOW

2 ON MY WAY

I haven't thought at all about my purpose or audience for the piece and, therefore, my voice falls flat. I'm pretty indifferent to the topic and it shows.

- I've put no energy into this piece.
- My purpose for writing this piece is a mystery to me, so I'm casting about aimlessly.
- Since my topic isn't interesting to me, chances are my piece won't be interesting to the reader. I haven't thought about my audience.
- I have taken no risks. There is no evidence that I find this topic interesting or care about it at all.

1 GETTING STARTED

Word Choice

the vocabulary you use to convey meaning and enlighten the reader

6 EXPERT

HIGH

The words and phrases I've selected are accurate, specific, and natural-sounding. My piece conveys precisely what I want to say, because of my powerful vocabulary.

- My piece contains strong verbs that bring it alive.
- I stretched by using the perfect words and phrases to convey my ideas.
- I've used content words and phrases with accuracy and precision.
- I've picked the best words and phrases, not just the first ones that came to mind.

5 WELL DONE

4 ALMOST THERE

MIDDLE

My words and phrases make sense but aren't very accurate, specific, or natural-sounding. The reader won't have trouble understanding them. However, he or she may find them uninspiring.

- I've used passive voice. I should rethink passages that contain passive voice and add "action words."
- I haven't come up with extraordinary ways to say ordinary things.
- My content words and phrases are accurate but general. I might have overused jargon. I need to choose words that are more precise.
- I need to revise this piece by replacing its weak words and phrases with strong ones.

3 MAKING STRIDES

2 ON MY WAY

LOW

My words and phrases are so unclear, the reader may wind up more confused than entertained, informed, or persuaded. I need to expand my vocabulary to improve this piece.

- My verbs are not strong. Passive voice permeates this piece.
- I've used bland words and phrases throughout—or the same words and phrases over and over.
- My content words are neither specific nor accurate enough to make the meaning clear.
- My words and phrases are not working; they distract the reader rather than guide him or her.

1 GETTING STARTED

Sentence Fluency

the way the text looks and sounds as it flows through your piece

6 EXPERT

HIGH

My piece is strong because I've written a variety of well-built sentences. I've woven those sentences together to create a smooth-sounding piece.

- I've constructed and connected my sentences for maximum impact.
- I've varied my sentence lengths and types—short and long, simple and complex.
- When I read my piece aloud, it is pleasing to my ear.
- I've broken grammar rules intentionally at points to create impact and interest.

5 WELL DONE

4 ALMOST THERE

MIDDLE

Although my sentences lack variety or creativity, most of them are grammatically correct. Some of them are smooth, while others are choppy and awkward.

- I've written solid shorter sentences. Now I need to try some longer ones.
- I've created different kinds of sentences, but the result is uneven.
- When I read my piece aloud, I stumble in a few places.
- Any sentences that break grammar rules are accidental and don't work well.

3 MAKING STRIDES

2 ON MY WAY

LOW

My sentences are choppy, incomplete, or rambling. I need to revise my piece extensively to make it more readable.

- Many of my sentences don't work because they're poorly constructed.
- I've used the same sentence lengths and types over and over again.
- When I read my piece aloud, I stumble in many places.
- If I've broken grammar rules, it's not for stylistic reasons—it's because I may not understand those rules.

1 GETTING STARTED

Conventions

the mechanical correctness of your piece, which helps guide the reader through the text

HIGH

6 EXPERT

My piece proves I can use a range of conventions with skill and creativity. It is ready for its intended audience.

- My spelling is strong. I've spelled all or nearly all the words accurately.
- I've used punctuation creatively and correctly and have begun new paragraphs in the right places.
- I've used capital letters correctly throughout my piece, even in tricky places.
- I've taken care to apply standard English grammar and usage.

5 WELL DONE

4 ALMOST THERE

MIDDLE

My writing still needs editing to correct problems in one or more conventions. I've stuck to the basics and haven't tried challenging conventions.

- I've misspelled words that I use all the time, as well as complex words that I don't use as often.
- My punctuation is basically strong, but I should review it one more time. I indented some of the paragraphs, but not all of them.
- I've correctly used capital letters in obvious places (such as the word *I*) but not in others.
- Even though my grammar and usage are not 100 percent correct, my audience should be able to read my piece.

3 MAKING STRIDES

2 ON MY WAY

LOW

The problems I'm having with conventions make this piece challenging to read, even for me! I've got lots of work to do before it's ready for its intended audience.

- Extensive spelling errors make my piece difficult to read and understand.
- I haven't punctuated or paragraphed the piece well, which makes it difficult for the reader to understand or enjoy my writing.
- My use of capital letters is so inconsistent, it's distracting.
- I need to clean up the piece considerably in terms of grammar and usage.

1 GETTING STARTED

Presentation

the physical appearance of your piece—the welcome mat that invites the reader in

6 EXPERT

HIGH

My piece's appearance makes it easy to read and enjoy. I've taken care to ensure that it is pleasing to my reader's eye.

- I've written clearly and legibly. My letters, words, and the spaces between them are uniform.
- My choice of font style, size, and/or color makes my piece a breeze to read.
- My margins frame the text nicely. There are no tears, smudges, or cross-outs.
- Text features such as bulleted lists, charts, pictures, and headers are working well.

5 WELL DONE

4 ALMOST THERE

MIDDLE

My piece still looks like a draft. Many visual elements should be cleaned up and handled with more care.

- My handwriting is readable, but my letters and words and the spaces between them should be treated more consistently.
- My choice of font style, size, and/or color seems "off"—inappropriate for my intended audience.
- My margins are uneven. There are some tears, smudges, or cross-outs.
- I've handled simple text features well but am struggling with the more complex ones.

3 MAKING STRIDES

2 ON MY WAY

LOW

My piece is almost unreadable because of its appearance. It's not ready for anyone but me to read.

- My handwriting is so hard to read, it creates a visual barrier.
- The font styles, sizes, and/or colors I've chosen are dizzying. They're not working.
- My margins are uneven or nonexistent, making the piece difficult to read.
- I haven't used text features well, even simple ones.

1 GETTING STARTED